Statement by the National Radiological Protection Board

Diagnostic Medical Exposures:
Advice on Exposure to
Ionising Radiation During Pregnancy

INTRODUCTION

1   The Board issued ASP8 in 1985 giving advice on the diagnostic exposure of women who are or who may be pregnant. While the current advice draws upon data published since 1985 the main objectives of Board advice are unchanged: to minimise the likelihood of inadvertent exposure of the conceptus before pregnancy is declared, and to prevent unnecessary exposure of the fetus when medical diagnostic procedures involving ionising radiation are indicated during pregnancy. In addition, the current advice should help to avoid unnecessary concern or action if an exposure does occur.

2   In providing this advice the Board has considered the risks to the developing embryo and fetus of death, malformation, mental impairment, cancer (solid tumours and leukaemias) and genetic damage from irradiation after the first missed menstrual period[1]. The possible risks from irradiation of the early (up to 3–4 weeks) conceptus and from gonadal irradiation of patients is also covered in the present advice[2].

3   Detailed information underlying this advice is given elsewhere.

DIAGNOSTIC EXAMINATION OF WOMEN OF REPRODUCTIVE CAPACITY

4   When a woman of reproductive age presents for diagnostic radiology in which the primary beam irradiates the pelvic area, or for procedures involving radioactive isotopes, appropriate steps should be taken to determine whether she is or may be pregnant, principally by requesting the date of the last menstrual period. If pregnancy is established or likely, justification for the proposed examination needs to be reviewed including whether the examination can be deferred, bearing in mind that a procedure of clinical benefit to the mother may also be of indirect benefit to her unborn child. In any resulting diagnostic examination it is important to keep the dose to the minimum consistent with diagnostic requirements.

5   For most diagnostic radiation exposures of the early conceptus the risks of cancer will be small; however, those few procedures yielding doses of some tens of milligray should be avoided, if possible, in early pregnancy. When the possibility of early pregnancy cannot be reasonably excluded, one way of avoiding such risks would be to restrict the use of high dose diagnostic procedures, such as barium enema, pelvic computed tomography (CT) or abdominal CT to the early part of the menstrual cycle when pregnancy is unlikely.

RISKS OF INDUCTION OF DEATH, GROSS MALFORMATION AND MENTAL IMPAIRMENT IN THE FETUS

6   In the light of the likely dose thresholds ascribed to these effects the Board considers that the doses resulting from most conventional diagnostic procedures have no substantial effect on the risk for the individual pregnancy regarding the incidence of fetal death, malformation or the impairment of mental development.

RISKS OF INDUCTION OF GENETIC DISEASE AND CANCER IN THE FETUS

7   The induction of genetic disease and cancer by ionising radiation is believed to show no dose threshold. The risks of these effects are judged relative to their natural incidences.

Genetic disease

8   For radiation-induced genetic disease expressing in the descendants of the unborn child the risk for any individual pregnancy following fetal irradiation from medical diagnostic procedures is judged by the Board to be small relative to the natural risk of genetic disease; thus, there is no indication for termination of pregnancy or for the use of invasive fetal diagnostic techniques (such as amniocentesis).

Cancer

9   For the expression of childhood cancer following irradiation of the fetus the Board considers that for most diagnostic procedures giving doses up to a few milligray, the associated risks are acceptable when compared with the natural risk. Therefore, exposure of the fetus in these circumstances is not considered to be a reason for termination of the pregnancy or for the use of invasive fetal diagnostic procedures.

10   For exposure of pregnant women to the higher doses (some tens of milligray) associated with, for example, pelvic CT, there may be more than a doubling of the natural cancer risk in the unborn child. This level of excess risk is about one in one-thousand for the individual fetus and is unlikely to be a reason for termination of the pregnancy or for the use of invasive fetal diagnostic procedures.

PRECONCEPTION RISKS TO PATIENTS

11   For gonadal exposure of the patient, dose minimisation through correct alignment, collimation and the use of gonadal shields whenever practical will minimise possible genetic effects. This advice applies to both female and male patients before and within the reproductive period. With appropriate gonadal dose minimisation, the risk of new mutations resulting from medical diagnostic exposures expressing as genetic disease in the descendants of patients is judged by the Board to be small, when compared for

DOCUMENTS OF THE NRPB

Di... **to**
Ioni... **ancy**

Est... **sks**

National Radiological Protection Board
Chilton, Didcot, Oxon OX11 0RQ

example with the risk of those arising naturally. The Board has also considered the question of possible cancer risk to offspring following parental gonadal irradiation. The current state of knowledge in this area is judged neither to provide grounds for recommending any restriction on post-exposure reproduction in patients having undergone medical diagnostic procedures nor to provide any reason for termination of resulting pregnancies or employing invasive fetal diagnostic procedures. Nevertheless, gonadal dose minimisation is recommended as a matter of simple prudence.

REFERENCES

1   NRPB. Estimates of late radiation risks to the UK population: Chapter 6—Irradiation *in utero. Doc. NRPB,* **4,** No. 4, 105–125 (1993).

2   NRPB. Diagnostic medical exposures: Exposure to ionising radiation of pregnant women. *Doc. NRPB,* **4,** No. 4, 5–14 (1993).

DIAGNOSTIC MEDICAL EXPOSURES: EXPOSURE TO IONISING RADIATION OF PREGNANT WOMEN

Biological Basis of the Board's Statement

ABSTRACT

The objectives of the revised Board advice on exposure to ionising radiation of pregnant women has as its objectives: to minimise the likelihood of inadvertent exposure of the conceptus before pregnancy is declared and to prevent unnecessary dose to the fetus. It should also help to avoid unnecessary concern or action if an exposure does occur. This report summarises the biological basis of the Board's Statement.

PREPARED BY R COX AND B H MacGIBBON

INTRODUCTION

1   The Board issued ASP8 'Exposure to ionising radiation of pregnant women: Advice on the diagnostic exposure of women who are, or who may be, pregnant' in 1985. This advice was generated in response to the ICRP 1984 statement[1] that no risks to the conceptus would follow irradiation during the first 10 days of the menstrual cycle and that subsequent risks in the remainder of the first 4 week period would be likely to be so small that no special limitation on exposure was required. Recent recommendations from ICRP maintain this position[2].

2   The Board has recently revised NRPB-R226—'Health effects models developed from the 1988 UNSCEAR report'[3]. This revised report[4] reviews the biological data on which current Board advice, on the diagnostic exposures to ionising radiation of women of reproductive age, is based. The conclusions concerning deterministic and stochastic effects of radiation on the developing embryo and fetus are summarised below.

3   In addition to risks of death, malformation, mental retardation, heritable effects and cancer resulting from irradiation *in utero* after the first missed menstrual period, present advice covers two other issues of particular relevance to diagnostic medical exposures: the possible risks from irradiation of the early conceptus and from preconception gonadal irradiation.

4   The objectives of the Board's advice are unchanged: to minimise the likelihood of inadvertent exposure of the conceptus before pregnancy is declared, and to prevent unnecessary dose to the fetus when medical diagnostic procedures involving ionising radiation are indicated during pregnancy. In addition, the current advice should also serve to prevent unnecessary concern or action if an exposure does occur.

DETERMINISTIC EFFECTS OF EXTERNAL RADIATIONS

5   Deterministic effects of radiation are those which result from damage to a number of cells in tissues, for which there is invariably a dose threshold. The principal

TABLE 1 *Estimates of threshold doses for deterministic effects following low LET in utero irradiation*[a]

Age (weeks)	Minimal dose (Gy) for:		
	Lethality	Gross malformations	Mental retardation (Japanese data)
0–1[b]	No threshold at day 1? 0.1 thereafter	No threshold at day 1?	No effects observed to about 8 weeks
2–5	0.25–0.5	0.2	
5–7	0.5	0.5	
7–21	> 0.5	Very few observed	Weeks 8–15: no threshold? Weeks 16–25: threshold dose 0.6–0.7 Gy
To term	> 1.0	Very few observed	Weeks 25–term: no effects observed

Notes

(a) Based on data cited in references 4–6, utilising information from human epidemiological studies and animal experiments.

(b) Up to about 7 days after conception.

? Indicates considerable uncertainty.

deterministic effects of external radiation on the developing embryo and fetus are death, malformation, growth retardation and abnormal brain development leading to severe mental retardation (SMR). Table 1 provides a summary of the acute radiation dose thresholds below which it is judged that there will be no such effects on the human embryo and fetus. Possible exceptions to this are animal data suggesting non-threshold type responses, following exposure of single cell zygotes, for the incidence of embryo-lethal events and, much less certainly, malformation. Data on Japanese atomic bomb survivors exposed *in utero* at gestation ages of 8–15 weeks also suggest the possibility of a non-threshold type response for the induction of SMR; this has not, however, been conclusively established although the data have been interpreted by ICRP as representing a loss of 30 IQ points per Gy (low LET)[2].

STOCHASTIC EFFECTS OF EXTERNAL RADIATION

6   Stochastic effects of radiation are those which have their origins in the probabilistic induction of damage to single cells in tissues and for which there is believed to be no dose threshold.

Heritable effects

7   In the absence of directly informative data, the Board[4] has assumed that the risk of heritable effects from *in utero* irradiation is the same as that applying after birth, ie $2.4 \times 10^{-2}\,\mathrm{Gy}^{-1}$ (low LET) (about 1 in 40 000 per mGy).

Cancer induction

8   The Board[4] considers that the number of excess cancer cases (leukaemias and solid tumours) to age 15 years following irradiation *in utero* should be taken as $6 \times 10^{-2}\,\mathrm{Gy}^{-1}$ (low LET). Since approximately 50% of all childhood cancers are fatal, the excess risk of cancer death is taken as $3 \times 10^{-2}\,\mathrm{Gy}^{-1}$ (about 1 in 33 000 per mGy). These data are summarised in Table 2. Estimation of the lifetime risk coefficient, for *in utero* irradiation, is subject to considerable uncertainty; it may exceed that for the first 15 years by a factor of about 2 to 4. It is therefore judged preferable, for the practical purpose of assessing risk of *in utero* medical exposure, to use the coefficient for risk to age 15 years.

TABLE 2 *Total risk of cancer up to age 15 years following in utero exposure ($10^{-2}\,Gy^{-1}$ low LET)*

Cancer type	Fatal	Non-fatal	Total
Leukaemia	1.25	1.25	2.5
Others	1.75	1.75	3.5
Total	3.0*	3.0	6.0

*About 1 in 33 000 per mGy.

Note
Based on UK national rates[7,8], the baseline risk of cancer in the first 15 years of life is around 1 in 650, ie about 1.5×10^{-3}. About half of these cancers are fatal.

9   Given its relevance to medical exposures, consideration is also given to cancer risk following exposure in early gestation. It is argued that although this cancer risk will be low it cannot be assumed to be zero.

ASSESSMENT OF *IN UTERO* DOSES

10   Table 3 provides data regarding mean and maximum fetal doses estimated from measurements made during national surveys conducted in the 1980s following various procedures in diagnostic radiology and nuclear medicine. Doses for the same type of procedure were seen to vary widely between patients and hospitals but, for the mean doses, the procedures giving the greatest fetal exposure are barium enemas, 16 mGy, and pelvic and abdominal computed tomography (CT), 25 and 8 mGy, respectively. For all other procedures listed in the table, the mean doses to the fetus are substantially lower.

	Fetal dose (mGy)	
Examination	Mean	Maximum
Conventional X-ray[9]		
Abdomen	2.6	18
Barium enema	16	80
Barium meal	2.8	—
Chest	<0.01	<0.01
Intravenous urography	3.2	20
Lumbar spine	3.2	12
Pelvis	1.7	8.0
Skull	<0.01	<0.01
Thoracic spine	<0.01	0.03
Computed tomography[10]		
Abdomen	8.0	49
Chest	0.06	0.96
Head	<0.005	<0.005
Lumbar spine	2.4	8.6
Pelvis	25	79
Pelvimetry	0.2	0.4
Nuclear medicine[11,12]		
^{99m}Tc bone scan (phosphate)	3.3	4.6
^{99m}Tc lung perfusion (MAA)	0.2	0.4
^{99m}Tc lung ventilation (aerosol)	0.3	1.2
^{99m}Tc kidney scan (DTPA)	1.5	4.0
^{99m}Tc thyroid scan (pertechnetate)	0.7	1.6
^{99m}Tc dynamic cardiac scan (RBC)	3.4	3.7
^{51}Cr glomerular filtration (EDTA)	<0.01	0.01
^{201}Tl myocardial perfusion (thallium)	3.7	4.0
^{99m}Tc brain scan (pertechnetate)	4.3	6.5

TABLE 3 *In utero doses following common diagnostic procedures; taken from Board surveys of diagnostic radiology and nuclear medicine*

Note Fetal doses cited are those assumed from estimates of uterine dose.

11   Fetal dosimetry from internal emitters is more complex than that for external sources, and the figures shown in the table for nuclear medicine procedures are based on estimates of the dose to the uterus from surrounding maternal organs with no

allowance for placental transfer of radionuclides to the fetus. Mean and maximum values correspond to the mean and maximum values of administered activity observed in the national survey of 1989/90[12].

IN UTERO RISKS FROM MEDICAL EXPOSURES
Deterministic effects

12   In practical terms, the threshold doses (Table 1) for the induction of death and gross malformation following *in utero* irradiation all lie well above the mean doses of Table 3 and are only approached by the maximum doses (about 80 mGy) noted in the case of barium enema and pelvic CT procedures. For the induction of mental retardation in offspring even an assumed no-threshold response in the 8–15 week period of gestation would not have important implications since for a maximum fetal dose of about 100 mGy the predicted three point IQ loss would be undetectable on an individual basis. In general, therefore, *in utero* doses have no implications for deterministic effects in an individual pregnancy.

Stochastic effects
Genetic disease

13   Table 4 illustrates the risk of new germ line mutations underlying genetic disease resulting from typical *in utero* diagnostic medical exposures; these are given as the probability of induced genetic disease per procedure on the basis of the mean doses of Table 3. The risks range from $4.0 \ 10^{-5}$ for pelvic X-ray exposures up to $6.1 \ 10^{-4}$ for pelvic CT. It may be seen that the majority of procedures carry risks of less than 10^{-4}; for a few procedures these risks can rise to around 10^{-3}. The natural frequency of genetic disease manifesting at birth in human populations has been estimated to be in the range 1%–3%, rising perhaps to 5%–6% if minor and somewhat uncertain congenital abnormalities ascertained in some studies are included[4]. Thus the increased genetic risk of 10^{-3} (0.1%) for an individual fetus associated with high dose diagnostic procedures is small compared with the natural risk of genetic disease. It should also be noted that the genetic risk coefficient of $2.4 \ 10^{-2} \ Gy^{-1}$ used in these calculations may tend to overestimate the frequency of induced genetic disease[4] and that the risk of genetic effects encompasses a diversity of disorders of widely differing severity; therefore this risk coefficient cannot be directly compared with that applying in the case of fatal cancer (see paragraphs 14 and 15).

Cancer

14   Table 4 illustrates the frequency of excess fatal cancer to age 15 years resulting from typical *in utero* medical exposures; these data and the derived risk coefficient of $3.0 \ 10^{-2} \ Gy^{-1}$ are chosen for risk estimation since the epidemiological evidence for cancer incidence and for lifetime cancer risk following *in utero* irradiation are considered to be less robust[4]. These *in utero* risks are given as the probability of excess disease per procedure on the basis of the mean doses of Table 3 and range from $5.1 \ 10^{-5}$ for pelvic X-rays up to $7.7 \ 10^{-4}$ for pelvic CT. The majority of radiological and nuclear medicine procedures carry risks of less than around $1.3 \ 10^{-4}$, but the risks of fatal childhood cancer of around 4.8–$7.7 \ 10^{-4}$ indicated for barium enema and pelvic CT procedures (with mean fetal doses of 16 and 25 mGy, respectively) should be regarded as significant since, although small, they are similar in magnitude to the natural

Exposure	Mean fetal doses[a] (mGy)	Probability of disease per mean exposure	
		Hereditary disease[b]	Fatal cancer to age 15 years[c]
X-ray			
Abdomen	2.6	$6.2\ 10^{-5}$	$7.7\ 10^{-5}$
Barium enema	16	$3.9\ 10^{-4}$	$4.8\ 10^{-4}$
Barium meal	2.8	$6.7\ 10^{-5}$	$8.4\ 10^{-5}$
Intravenous urography	3.2	$7.7\ 10^{-5}$	$9.6\ 10^{-5}$
Lumbar spine	3.2	$7.6\ 10^{-5}$	$9.5\ 10^{-5}$
Pelvis	1.7	$4.0\ 10^{-5}$	$5.1\ 10^{-5}$
Computed tomography			
Abdomen	8.0	$1.9\ 10^{-4}$	$2.4\ 10^{-4}$
Lumbar spine	2.4	$5.7\ 10^{-5}$	$7.1\ 10^{-5}$
Pelvis	25	$6.1\ 10^{-4}$	$7.7\ 10^{-4}$
Nuclear medicine			
^{99}Tc bone scan	3.3	$0.79\ 10^{-4}$	$1.0\ 10^{-4}$
^{99}Tc brain scan	4.3	$1.0\ 10^{-4}$	$1.3\ 10^{-4}$

TABLE 4 *Risk of hereditary disease and cancer following typical in utero diagnostic medical exposure to radiation*

Notes
(a) Data of Table 3.
(b) Using a risk coefficient of $2.4\ 10^{-2}$ Gy (from reference 4).
(c) Using a risk coefficient of $3.0\ 10^{-2}$ Gy (from reference 4).

cumulative risk of fatal childhood cancer in England and Wales to age 15 years, estimated to be about $7.7\ 10^{-4}$ (1 in 1300)[7,8]. In the case of undeclared pregnancy, where gestational age may be up to 3–4 weeks, the Board[4] has argued that cancer risk, whilst not zero, will tend to be much lower than in the subsequent phases of fetogenesis.

15   The use of natural cumulative cancer risk for comparison with *in utero* fatal cancer induction applies specifically to disease manifesting by age 15 years. Since this natural risk will rise with age, reaching 20%–25% over a lifetime, such risk comparison is deemed inappropriate for judging the acceptability, or otherwise, of lifetime risks. Nevertheless, it may be noted that, even if the lifetime risk of *in utero* induced fatal cancer is as much as four times greater than that to age 15 years, judgements based on comparing induced risks with natural risks to 15 years will be conservative; while an *in utero* dose of about 25 mGy will double the natural risk of fatal cancer to age 15 years, it will only result in a lifetime fatal cancer risk of less than 0.5%, compared with the natural level of risk of 20%–25%.

PRECONCEPTION DOSES TO PATIENTS AND CANCER IN THE OFFSPRING

16   On the basis of current knowledge, the findings of Gardner *et al*[13] of excess leukaemia in the offspring of certain exposed male radiation workers are not considered to be sufficiently compelling to prompt specific recommendations regarding possible preconception risk to the offspring[4]. There are no human data

regarding such preconception effects of radiation in women. Any restriction in the use of beneficial medical diagnostic procedures, on the basis of such possible risks from preconception exposures, is considered by the Board to be inappropriate since the risk, which remains unproven, may not in fact exist.

CONCLUSIONS AND RECOMMENDATIONS

17   The specific recommendations, below, to meet the objectives outlined in paragraph 4 should be viewed in the general context of other relevant reports[14,15] and the recommendations of a joint working party of the Royal College of Radiologists and the Board on patient dose reduction[16], together with the Board's suggested national reference dose levels[17], the recently published protocol for patient dose measurements in diagnostic radiology[18], and the advice of the Administration of Radioactive Substances Advisory Committee[19].

Diagnostic examination of women of reproductive capacity

18   When a woman of reproductive age presents for diagnostic radiology or procedures involving radioactive isotopes, appropriate steps should be taken to determine whether she is or may be pregnant, principally by requesting the date of the last menstrual period. If pregnancy is established or likely, justification for the proposed examination needs to be reviewed, including whether the examination can be deferred, bearing in mind that a procedure of clinical benefit to the mother may also be of indirect benefit to her unborn child. In any resulting diagnostic examination it is important to keep the fetal dose to the minimum consistent with diagnostic requirements.

19   It is important whenever possible to estimate the actual fetal dose rather than use a mean fetal dose for a procedure. The maximum dose for a given procedure may be greater than the mean by a factor of between two and ten. Only in the case of some conventional X-ray examinations, such as those to the chest or thoracic spine, and in dental procedures, can it be assumed that even a maximum dose from the procedure would be less than a few milligray (Table 3).

20   In the case of nuclear medicine procedures, although differences also exist between mean and maximum doses, fewer common procedures are likely to involve fetal doses of more than a few milligray.

Deterministic effects

21   In the light of the likely dose thresholds ascribed to these effects the Board considers that the doses resulting from most conventional diagnostic procedures have no substantial effect on the risk to the individual pregnancy regarding the incidence of fetal death, malformation or the impairment of mental development.

Stochastic effects

22   The induction of genetic disease and cancer by ionising radiation is believed to show no dose threshold. The risks of these effects are judged relative to their natural incidences.

Heritable disease

23   For radiation-induced genetic disease expressing in the descendants of the unborn child the risk for any individual pregnancy following fetal irradiation from medical

diagnostic procedures is judged by the Board to be small relative to the natural risk of genetic disease; thus, there is no indication for termination of pregnancy or for the use of invasive fetal diagnostic techniques (such as amniocentesis).

Cancer induction

24 For the expression of childhood cancer following irradiation of the fetus the Board considers that for most diagnostic procedures giving doses up to a few millgray the associated risks are acceptable when compared with the natural risk. Therefore exposure of the fetus in these circumstances is not considered to be a reason for termination of the pregnancy or for the use of invasive fetal diagnostic procedures.

25 For exposure of pregnant women to the higher doses (some tens of milligray) associated with, for example, pelvic CT, there may be more than a doubling of the natural cancer risk in the unborn child. This level of excess risk is about one in one-thousand for the individual fetus and is unlikely to be a reason for termination of the pregnancy or for the use of invasive fetal diagnostic procedures.

26 For most diagnostic radiation exposures of the early conceptus the risks of cancer will be small; however, those few procedures yielding doses of some tens of milligray should be avoided, if possible, even in early pregnancy. When the possibility of early pregnancy cannot be reasonably excluded, one way of avoiding such risks would be to restrict the use of high dose diagnostic procedures such as barium enema, pelvic computerised tomography (CT), abdominal CT or even some plain-field techniques involving the pelvis, to the early part of the menstrual cycle when pregnancy is unlikely.

27 In those few cases where irradiation during the early part of the menstrual cycle is deemed to be necessary there may, however, be an increased risk of genetic damage to potentially radiosensitive pre-ovulatory oocytes of the patient[20]. Such radiosensitivity has been observed in the mouse[21] but is probably of short duration and uncertain origin and therefore cannot be readily used to assess risks in women.

Preconception risks to patients

28 For gonadal exposure of the patient, dose minimisation through correct alignment, collimation and the use of gonadal shields whenever practical will minimise possible genetic effects[14,15]. This advice applies to both female and male patients, especially if below reproductive age. With appropriate gonadal dose minimisation, the risk of new mutations resulting from medical diagnostic exposures expressing as genetic disease in the descendants of patients is judged by the Board to be small compared with the risk of those arising naturally. The Board has also considered the question of possible cancer risk to offspring following parental gonadal irradiation. The current state of knowledge in this area is not judged to provide grounds for recommending any restriction on post-exposure reproduction in patients having undergone medical diagnostic procedures or to provide any reason for termination of resulting pregnancies or employing invasive fetal diagnostic procedures. Nevertheless, gonadal dose minimisation is recommended as a matter of simple prudence.

Radiotherapy

29 The Board does not consider it appropriate to draw up advice on the exposure of women who are, or may be, pregnant to ionising radiation in the course of radiotherapy. However, the general principles outlined above apply and both the thresholds suggested for deterministic effects and the specific risk factors given for heritable

disease and cancer induction may be used to assess the possible risks to the fetus arising from *in utero* irradiation in the course of radiotherapy.

REFERENCES

1   ICRP. Statement from the 1983 Washington meeting of ICRP. *Ann. ICRP,* **14,** No. 1 (1984).

2   ICRP. 1990 Recommendations of the International Commission on Radiological Protection. *Ann. ICRP,* **21,** Nos 1–3 (1991).

3   Stather, J W, Muirhead, C R, Edwards, A A, Harrison, J D, Lloyd, D C, and Wood, N R. Health effects models developed from the 1988 UNSCEAR report. Chilton, NRPB-R226 (1988).

4   NRPB. Estimates of late radiation risks to the UK population. *Doc. NRPB,* **4,** No. 4, 15–157 (1993).

5   Brent, R L, Beckman, D A, and Jensh, R P. Relative radiosensitivity of fetal tissues. *Adv. Radiat. Biol.,* **12,** 239–42 (1987).

6   Muller, W U, and Streffer C. Lethal and teratogenic effects after exposure to X-rays at various times of early murine gestation. *Teratology,* **42,** 643–50 (1990).

7   OPCS. Mortality Statistics, Cause. London, HMSO, Series DH2, No. 14 (1989).

8   OPCS. Cancer Statistics, Registrations. London, HMSO, Series MB1, No. 16 (1988).

9   Shrimpton, P C, Wall, B F, Jones, D G, Fisher, E S, Hillier, M C, Kendall, G M, and Harrison, R M. A national survey of doses to patients undergoing a selection of routine X-ray examinations in English hospitals. Chilton, NRPB-R200 (1986) (London, HMSO).

10   Shrimpton, P C, Jones, D G, Hillier, M C, Wall, B F, Le Heron, J C, and Faulkner, K. Survey of CT practice in the UK. Part 2: Dosimetric aspects. Chilton, NRPB-R249 (1991) (London, HMSO).

11   Wall, B F, Hillier, M C, and Kendall, G M. Nuclear medicine activity in the United Kingdom. *Br. J. Radiol.,* **58,** 125 (1985).

12   Elliott, A T, and Shields, R A. Nuclear medicine survey, 1989/90. *Nuclear Medicine Communications* (to be published).

13   Gardner, M J, Snee, M P, Hall, A J, Powell, C A, Downes, S, and Terrell, J D. Results of case control study of leukaemia and lymphoma among young people near Sellafield nuclear plant in West Cumbria. *Br. Med. J.,* **300,** 423–9 (1990).

14   ICRP. Protection of the patient in diagnostic radiology. ICRP Publication 34. *Ann. ICRP,* **9,** Nos 2–3 (1982).

15   NRPB/HSE/DHSS/DHSS(NI)/SHHD/WO. Guidance Notes for the protection of persons against ionising radiations arising from medical and dental use. Chilton, NRPB (1988) (London, HMSO).

16   NRPB/RCR. Patient dose reduction in diagnostic radiology. *Doc. NRPB,* **1,** No. 3 (1990).

17   Shrimpton, P C, Wall, B F, and Hillier, M C. Suggested guideline doses for medical x-ray examinations. IN Radiation Protection Theory and Practice. Proceedings 4th International Symposium of SRP (Ed. E P Goldfinch). Bristol, IOPP (1989).

18   IPSM/NRPB/CoR. National protocol for patient dose measurements in diagnostic radiology. Chilton, NRPB (1992).

19   ARSAC. Notes for guidance on the administration of radioactive substances to persons for purposes of diagnosis, treatment or research. London, Department of Health (to be published).

20   Russell, J G B. Pregnancy and ionising radiation. *Br. Med. J.,* **305,** 1172 (1992).

21   Tease, C, and Fisher, G. X-ray-induced chromosome aberrations in immediately pre-ovulating oocytes. *Mutat. Res.,* **173,** 211–15 (1986).

ESTIMATES OF LATE RADIATION RISKS TO THE UK POPULATION

ABSTRACT

This publication provides a review of information for assessing stochastic effects (cancer and hereditary disease) and the effects of irradiation *in utero* that are likely to arise in the UK population following exposure to external radiation, or as a result of intakes of radionuclides. It updates information in the report NRPB-R226. Since the publication of that report in 1988 more detailed information from follow-up of the Japanese atomic bomb survivors has been released, the 1990 Recommendations of ICRP have been published and the first analysis of the UK National Registry for Radiation Workers, which provides direct evidence on the risks from low dose and low dose rate occupational exposures, has been completed. Important elements in these publications concern: the appropriate choice of projection models and the DDREF for estimating lifetime cancer risks and the assessment of dose–response relationship for mental retardation resulting from *in utero* exposure to radiation. The development of risk models which take account of mechanisms of carcinogenesis has also received more attention in recent years.

Throughout this review the aim has been to present a scientific rather than a conservative assessment, and to provide information about the uncertainties involved. The UK specific risk factors developed in this report for cancer induction are not intended to replace the values that ICRP has developed for setting standards in radiation protection. They are, however, intended for use in calculating late health effects within a UK population, for example, in accident consequence assessments or in determining probability of causation.

There is little new information about deterministic effects and earlier Board publications (NRPB-R226 and NRPB-M246) will continue to be available until such time as early effects data are reviewed.

PREPARED BY C R MUIRHEAD, R COX, J W STATHER,
B H MacGIBBON, A A EDWARDS AND R G E HAYLOCK

1 Introduction

1   This publication provides an update of the review of information for assessing health effects likely to arise in the UK population following exposure to external radiation, or as a result of intakes of radionuclides, published as NRPB-R226[1], in 1988.

2   Since then more detailed information from follow-up of the Japanese atomic bomb survivors has been released by the Radiation Effects Research Foundation in Hiroshima (RERF) and the BEIR V Committee[2] has used this information to examine a variety of risk models. Subsequently, the 1990 Recommendations of ICRP have been published[3]. Also the first analysis of the UK National Registry for Radiation Workers, which provides direct evidence on the risks from low dose and low dose rate occupational exposures, has been completed[4]. Finally, reconsideration of the appropriate value for the dose and dose rate effectiveness factor (DDREF) to be applied in extrapolating results from high dose and high dose rate studies to provide information about effects at low doses and low dose rates, has been undertaken by ICRP[3] and UNSCEAR will be reviewing DDREF in its next publication.

3   Important elements in these recent publications concern:

(i)   the appropriate choice of projection models and the DDREF for estimating lifetime cancer risks, together with the ICRP recommendation that risk coefficients for application in radiation protection should be increased,

(ii) assessment of the dose–response relationship for mental retardation resulting from *in utero* exposure to radiation.

The development of risk models which take account of mechanisms of carcinogenesis has also received more attention in recent years.

4   For all these reasons, revision of those parts of NRPB-R226 dealing with stochastic effects (cancer and hereditary disease) and the effects of irradiation *in utero* is now needed. The issues of mechanisms of carcinogenesis and dose and dose rate effectiveness factors are discussed in Chapters 2 and 3, respectively.

5   There is little new information about deterministic effects, and those parts of NRPB-R226 dealing with early effects have not been revised. Dose–response relationships for additional early health effects (such as thyroid effects, lens opacities and sterility) have been discussed in NRPB-M246[5]. These Board publications will continue to be available until such time as early effects are reviewed.

6   The general principles set out in NRPB-R226 for assessing the late health effects of radiation still apply. Throughout this review the aim has been to present a scientific rather than a conservative assessment, and to provide information about the uncertainties involved. The UK–specific risk factors developed in this report for cancer induction are not intended to replace the values that ICRP[3] has developed for setting standards in radiation protection. They are, however, intended for use in calculating late health effects within a UK population, for example, in accident consequence assessments or in determining probability of causation. Particular attention has also been given to reviewing the risk to the developing embryo and fetus.

REFERENCES

1 Stather, J W, Muirhead, C R, Edwards, A A, Harrison, J D, Lloyd, D C, and Wood, N R. Health effect models developed from the 1988 UNSCEAR report. Chilton, NRPB-R226 (1988) (London, HMSO).

2 BEIR V. Health effects of exposure to low levels of ionising radiation. Washington DC, NAS/NRC (1990).

3 ICRP. 1990 Recommendations of the International Commission on Radiological Protection. ICRP Publication 60, *Ann. ICRP*, **21**, Nos 1–3 (1991).

4 Kendall, G M, Muirhead, C R, MacGibbon, B H, O'Hagan, J A, Conquest, A J, Goodill, A A, Butland, B K, Fell, T P, Jackson, D A, Webb, M A, Haylock, R G E, Thomas, J M, and Silk, T J. First analysis of the National Registry for Radiation Workers: Occupational exposure to ionising radiation and mortality. Chilton, NRPB-R251 (1992) (London, HMSO).

5 Saunders, R D, Ellender, M, Kowalczuk, C I, Sienkiewicz, Z J, and Wood, N R. Dose–response relationships for early and continuing health effects. Chilton, NRPB-M246 (1990).

2 Mechanisms of Radiation Tumorigenesis

INTRODUCTION

1   During the last few years there has been a substantial increase in knowledge of cellular and molecular mechanisms of tumorigenesis (see, for example, references 1–8). Of particular importance to an understanding of radiation tumorigenesis is the knowledge that, for the majority of human and animal tumours, tumour initiation processes probably involve specific changes to single target cells in tissue but that tumour development is far more complex and involves multistage clonal growth and evolution before the final malignant state is achieved. Thus, multistage tumour development and its variation between tumour types may, in part, explain the different latent periods seen in radiation-induced tumours of man and experimental animals. Although there is evidence that specific mechanisms for induction can vary amongst tumours, the malignant process may be broadly divided into three phases: initiation, promotion and progression. It should be recognised, however, that these are operational definitions and that in most *in vivo* circumstances there are not clearly defined boundaries between these phases.

TUMOUR INITIATION, PROMOTION AND PROGRESSION

Initiation

2   There is compelling evidence:

  (i)   for the single cell (monoclonal) origin of most tumours,
  (ii) that the principal target for initiation resides in cellular DNA,
  (iii) that tumour initiating events are, in general, stable and may persist in tissues for long periods.

Thus it seems probable that the majority of initiating events for tumorigenesis are mutations affecting the activity of a single or limited set of genes in a given target cell. Such somatic cell mutations are then believed to provide carrier cells with some form of growth or selective advantage such that they have the potential to evade some of the normal tissue constraints and proliferate to form clones of pre-neoplastic cells. It is currently believed that cells having stem-like properties are the principal targets for the induction of tumour initiating events.

3   On the basis of current knowledge, two basic categories of tumour initiating mutations may be envisaged:

  (i)   mutational activation of so-called proto-oncogenes leading to positive functional changes in cellular regulation, eg *increased activity or altered specificity* of a gene involved in growth stimulation[2,3].
  (ii) mutational inactivation or loss of so-called tumour suppressor genes leading to negative functional changes in cellular regulation, eg loss of activity of a gene involved in growth inhibition[5,8].

4   For both these cases it is the status of the gene product that is critical for cellular change. While such changes in the structure and activity of proto-oncogenes and tumour suppressor genes and their protein products have been characterised in a range of human and animal tumours, it is inherently difficult to determine whether these events initiated the tumour or played roles in malignant development. Some progress has, however, been made in the identification of early events in human and animal tumorigenesis and Table 2.1 provides examples of such gene-specific changes in human tumours. Whilst far from providing a complete picture, these data indicate that, although different tumours are often characterised by different early events, some tumours share common genetic changes.

5   The weight of current evidence deriving from molecular genetic studies of cancer predisposition in man[8] and the molecular characteristics of human tumours associated with known exposure to environmental carcinogens[19-23] tend to support the argument that specific gene loss or inactivation plays the principal role in tumour initiation. In particular, it has been shown that the spectrum of *p53* tumour suppressor gene mutations in the lung tumours of radon-exposed uranium miners is markedly different from that seen in tobacco-related disease[23]. This observation lends support to the contention that many of these tumours are indeed induced by alpha particle damage to target respiratory cells. Although not of specific relevance to the risk estimates presented in this document, the molecular associations established between such environmental exposures and organ-specific cancer may have long-term implications for establishing tumour causality in some radiation-exposed human populations. The Board recognises the importance of these new molecular epidemiological approaches which may, in the longer term, contribute significantly to the assessment of cancer risk in irradiated human populations (see also Harris[24]).

Promotion

6   While the tumorigenic activity of agents such as ionising radiation, ultraviolet radiation (UVR) and certain chemical agents may be correlated with their capacity to induce damage to chromosomal DNA, some non-genotoxic chemicals appear to act as co-carcinogens, ie alone they exhibit little or no tumorigenic activity but in concert they are able to promote the development of induced tumours. Generally, such agents share the capacity of inducing a degree of hyperplasia in treated tissues and a current view is that this property stems from changes that they induce in the expression of growth enhancing genes in cells. Thus dormant tumour initiated cells in tissues may be stimulated to proliferate and express their pre-neoplastic growth advantage and, in this way, promotion is evidenced by an increase in the frequency of induced neoplasia[25,26].

7   Tumour promoting agents vary greatly in structure and origin and range from phorbol esters and bile acids to cellular growth factors, hormones and ill-defined dietary/environmental factors. Many of these agents recognise and interact with specific protein receptors on cell membranes and it is this specific interaction that triggers gene expression changes. Experimental studies suggest that genes of the protein kinase C family play an important role in these promotional processes. It is important to stress here that, unlike tumour initiation, promotion does not rely upon the induction of stable cellular changes; in general, chronic or repeated exposure to the promoting agent is necessary to elicit the maximum response, ie dose–response

TABLE 2.1 *Examples of early genetic changes and pre-disposing genes in human tumorigenesis*

Genetic change	Tumour type	Target gene(s) (chromosomal location)	Genetic predisposition	References
Chromosomal translocations				
Translocation 9→22	Chronic myeloid leukaemia	*abl*(9) activation	—	9
Translocation 18→14	Follicular B-lymphoma	*bcl-2*(18) activation	—	9,10
Translocation 10→14	T-acute lymphocytic leukaemia	*HOX*-11(10) deregulation	—	11
Chromosomal deletion				
	Myelodysplastic disorders	? (deletion 5/7)	—	12
Deletion or point mutation of genes [*]				
	Retinoblastoma/osteosarcoma	*RB*(13) loss	Retinoblastoma	1,5
	Nephroblastoma	*WT*(11) loss	WAGR syndrome	5
	Neurofibroma/CNS tumours	*NF*-1(17) loss	Neurofibromatosis	5,13
	Colorectal carcinoma	*MCC*(5) *APC*(5) loss	Familial adenomatous polyposis	6,14–16
	Range of solid tumours	*p53*(17) loss	Li-Fraumeni syndrome	5,17,53
	Mammary/ovarian carcinoma	? (17)	Early-onset familial disease	18

[*]For some of these genes, inactivation resulting from mutation may in some tumours involve deletions visible at the chromosome level.

relationships are markedly different from that seen with initiating agents. Recently, however, there has been some re-evaluation of the mechanisms of action of some of the more powerful promotors such as the phorbol ester, TPA. For this agent it now appears that, in addition to inducing tissue hyperplasia, there may also be an induction of intracellular DNA damaging processes such as those associated with the production of reactive chemical radicals. In addition, there is growing evidence that some tumour promoting agents reduce the potential for cell-to-cell communication, perhaps reducing the capacity of normal cells in tissues to moderate the growth of neighbouring neoplastic precursors[26].

Progression

8   There is increasing evidence that the majority of induced pre-neoplastic cells in tissues do not progress to frank malignancy and, depending on tumour type, a series of secondary chromosomal and gene mutations is necessary to complete the evolutionary process. These mutations may, for example, block the normal pathways of terminal cellular differentiation, alter cell cycle controls and response to growth regulating factors, enhance the recruitment of a blood supply or change the mobility of cells such that they become invasive and metastatic[27,28]. Changes to specific proto-oncogene and tumour suppressor genes have been found to be associated with these secondary changes but these will not be discussed here.

9   In the main, the acquisition of these stable and irreversible changes within an evolving neoplastic population of cells probably occurs spontaneously and there is evidence that increased genomic instability may be an inherent feature of many tumour cells. There is, however, experimental evidence that malignant conversion and progression may be increased and/or accelerated by exposure of pre-neoplastic cells in tissue to genotoxic agents; for ionising radiation such effects have so far only been demonstrated at relatively high doses.

Conclusions

10   There is now unambiguous evidence for the multistage nature of tumour induction and this has provided an impetus for the development of mathematical models that seek broadly to describe this complex biological process (see Chapter 4). In this context it is important to stress that the number of steps required for cellular commitment to full malignant conversion will vary between tumour types; for example, in the case of the childhood tumours, retinoblastoma and Wilms kidney tumour, that number may be only two[1], while in the case of colorectal cancer (which has a long latent period) as many as five to ten steps have been suggested[6]. At present, theoretical modelling of multistage carcinogenesis is at an early phase of development largely because of the uncertainties on the number of stages involved and the temporal relationship between them. The evidence outlined below tends to point towards low dose radiation acting at an early initiation stage of carcinogenesis but this may not be true in all circumstances. Consequently, while illustrations of the possible modelling approaches are provided in Chapter 4, none of these is considered to be sufficiently well founded to be used for risk projection purposes. While mechanistic studies on radiation tumorigenesis will increasingly contribute to risk estimation it is important to recognise that evolving knowledge in this area will always need to be coupled with soundly based epidemiological data.

ROLE OF IONISING RADIATION IN TUMORIGENESIS

11   Ionising radiation is a relatively well-characterised mutagenic agent in mammalian somatic cells (see, for example, reference 29). Since both tumour initiation and progression are characterised by acquisition of specific cellular mutations, it may be expected that ionising radiation plays a role throughout the malignant process. There are, however, reasons for believing that at low doses the principal point of action is early in the malignant process, probably at the initiation stage, and that the target cell population is likely to be relatively uncommitted 'stem-like' cells in tissues.

12   Analyses of current data for 'solid' cancers increasingly favour the application of empirically based multiplicative rather than additive risk models to the cancer incidence recorded in the survivors of the Japanese atomic bomb explosions. Many such multiplicative models incorporate the fundamental assumption of a constant relative risk over time since exposure. This assumption is broadly consistent with radiation acting as an initiating agent[30]. In contrast, if epidemiological analyses had revealed a pattern of cancer induction rates increasing with age at exposure then a significant role for radiation in tumour promotion/progression might be predicted. Specifically, if radiation exposure principally increased the probability that existing pre-neoplastic clones in tissues would convert to full malignancy then, on the basis of the expected accumulation with time of spontaneously arising pre-neoplastic cells, it would be predicted that induced cancer rates would increase with age at exposure – also, that radiation-induced cancers might have shorter latency periods. These expectations are not met either in analysis of the Japanese data or in the majority of radiation tumorigenesis studies with animals. Indeed, there is increasing evidence that, for some tumours, the reverse may apply, ie that there is increased susceptibility at younger ages (see Chapter 4). Although still uncertain, such findings may reflect the age-dependent activity of target stem cells in developing tissues, such that at younger ages certain developing tissues contain the maximum concentration of sensitive targets for tumour initiation, and that this concentration either declines with age or that there is a significant reduction in the probability of malignant development. At present this argument may be most clearly applied to the breast, thyroid and colon where age-dependent susceptibility in man is most clearly evident; in addition, there is experimental evidence of the persistence of (chemically) induced pre-neoplastic cells in animal breast tissues which are subsequently mobilised through age-dependent hormone-mediated promotional processes[31]. A process involving age-dependent haemopoietic development has also been proposed in order to explain the incidence and age distribution of some spontaneously arising childhood leukaemias[32].

13   Thus a cogent argument may be assembled in support of the contention that, particularly at *low doses*, ionising radiation acts principally as an initiating agent for tumorigenesis. This, together with experimental evidence on the single cell origin of cancer and the involvement of single target genes in the initiation process, has major implications for radiological protection. Briefly, such a mechanism of action implies that the traversal of a single ionising radiation track through a single target cell has a low, but finite, probability of inducing a pre-neoplastic change; hence for tumour initiation even at very low doses there is no *a priori* expectation of a threshold effect. This should be contrasted with *hypothetical* mechanisms involving:

(i)   radiation acting as a tumour promoting agent,

(ii) a multicell origin for tumorigenesis,

(iii) a strict multigene mutational mechanism for initiation,

all of which might predict a multitrack basis for tumour induction and, through this, the likelihood of a low dose threshold for radiation tumorigenesis. In this context, the influence of post-irradiation cellular repair on tumour initiation is discussed below. These rather simplistic arguments tend to ignore the potential complexity of the initiation process but succeed in providing a relatively straightforward cellular foundation on which to construct empirical models of cancer risk at low doses and low dose rates.

TUMOUR INITIATION AT THE MOLECULAR LEVEL

14   If, as proposed, ionising radiation acts principally as a mutagenic agent for specific genes involved in tumour initiation then it is important to consider further the possible mechanisms governing the initiation process and how this might relate to the known mutagenic action of radiation. Known features of proto-oncogene and tumour suppressor gene mutations will now be considered in an attempt to relate the mutagenic changes in cellular DNA that potentially initiate neoplastic transformation to the size of the DNA target that these events present to single ionising tracks of radiation.

15   Activation of proto-oncogenes, which is a genetically dominant change in cells, may be considered to occur via two principal mechanisms:

(i)   point mutations affecting a very limited set of DNA base pairs (bp)* within a target gene, eg proto-oncogenes of the *ras* family[2] – here the molecular target for radiation action will tend to be very small, say about 10 bp,

(ii) gene-specific chromosome translocations involving the juxtaposition of the proto-oncogene, eg *abl* and *bcl*-2[4,9,10], with another specific and activating DNA sequence – here the molecular target may be larger, say 10^2 to 10^4 bp but the event may involve damage at two independent sites in the genome.

Thus, relative to the size of the whole cellular genome (about 10^9 bp), gene activation processes (i) and (ii) both present extremely small targets for single ionising radiation tracks.

16   In contrast, tumour suppressor genes, eg *RB, WT* and *p53* (Table 2.1) potentially provide much larger DNA targets, ranging in size perhaps from 10^4 to 10^7 bp, ie up to whole chromosome segments. Most tumour suppressor genes are located on autosomal chromosomes and are, in principle, recessive in their function such that it is necessary to lose both gene copies from the cell in order to effect full neoplastic transformation. However, recent proposals have included mechanisms whereby loss or inactivation of even one copy may result in a pre-neoplastic cellular change[7,8,33]. On the basis of such mechanistic considerations it becomes possible therefore to suggest that, through presenting much larger DNA targets, the loss of tumour suppressor genes

---

*The pairing of aromatic nucleotide bases in DNA provides the underlying genetic code; there are about 10^9 base pairs in the haploid genome of each mammalian cell and each genome has a physical length approaching 2 nm.

may be a more frequent form of radiation-induced tumour initiation than that associated with proto-oncogene activation. A practical implication of this hypothesis is that the relative inducibility of human tumours by radiation may depend critically on their requirement for initiation and, here, it may be expected that the induction of gene-loss dependent tumours will tend to be favoured. It is recognised, however, that this rather simplistic 'target size' hypothesis may not apply in the case of mutations induced by indirect mechanisms involving, perhaps, the induction of DNA misrecombination or misreplication of certain DNA sequences following the induction of damage elsewhere in the genome.

17   Molecular analysis of radiation-induced mutations in well-characterised genes in cultured mammalian cells adds further weight to the argument that gene loss may preferentially underly the induction of tumours by radiation. These analyses show that radiation is a relatively weak point mutagen but is far more efficient at inducing gene and chromosomal deletions (see, for example, reference 29). However, on this point it is important to recognise that the specific chromosomal location of target genes and the genetic background of the target cell may have profound effects on both the frequency of induced mutation and the spectrum of mutational events seen. For example, if target gene function is critical for cell viability then only point mutations that produce subtle changes in that function will be tolerated. Also, that the weak activity of ionising radiation as a point mutagen noted above is judged in the context of its far greater capacity to induce DNA deletion/rearrangement rather than its relationship to other genotoxic agents.

INFLUENCE OF POST-IRRADIATION CELLULAR REPAIR SYSTEMS

18   Cells have evolved complex enzyme-mediated systems in order to identify and repair damage to their chromosomal DNA. Such damage may occur spontaneously in the course of DNA replication and endogenous metabolism but may also be induced by exogenous genotoxic agents such as UVR, ionising radiation and certain chemicals. DNA damage may be repaired with total fidelity, ie error-free repair, thus restoring DNA sequences to their normal state, or be misrepaired so that DNA strand integrity is restored but at the expense of changes to DNA sequences, ie error-prone repair leading to DNA base pair changes, deletions and rearrangements at or close to the site of damage. It may be seen therefore that error-free repair does not increase the frequency of mutational events in surviving cells while the converse applies when repair is error-prone[34].

19   There is accumulating evidence that the enzyme systems that act on damage induced by ionising radiation differ from those that act on damage induced by UVR and most chemical agents, implying that there are differences in the nature of biologically critical DNA damage. This is evidenced by studies on cells from patients with the radiosensitive human genetic disorder, ataxia-telangiectasia (A-T), which have been shown to be hypersensitive to X-rays and gamma rays but not to UVR and the vast majority of chemical agents; broadly, the converse applies in the case of the sun-sensitive human disorder, xeroderma pigmentosum[34-36].

20   Studies on the nature and repair of DNA damage induced by ionising radiation in mammalian cells strongly suggest that repair of double strand breaks in DNA is critical for the maintenance of normal biological functions. Many radiosensitive mutants of

cultured mammalian cells, including human A-T, show defects in the repair of these breaks. In the case of A-T this defect may centre on the increased frequency with which the breaks are rejoined incorrectly leading to chromosomal aberrations and DNA deletions[37,38].

21   In the context of this document, a most important observation with such radiosensitive strains of mammalian cells is that the genetically determined DNA repair defect is also manifest in the loss or reduction of dose rate effects for cell inactivation. It appears therefore that dose rate effects may be principally determined by cellular DNA repair functions which may be viewed as operating with greater fidelity when DNA damage is sustained at a low rate[38,39]. However, whether such changes in repair apply to a single lesion type or interacting lesions remains uncertain. None of the above studies provides any evidence that cellular DNA repair can provide a low radiation dose threshold for cellular effect at the level of DNA damage expression. Indeed, if, as implied above, DNA double strand breaks are critical lesions for cellular radiation effects then, even under optimal conditions leading to the correct repair of the vast majority of breaks, total repair fidelity may never be achieved. Such high fidelity repair of DNA damage might only be expected when an undamaged complementary DNA sequence template is available to copy damaged sequences lost or excised from the other. When both strands are damaged at the same point by the passage of an ionising radiation track then some degree of misrepair should be expected. Many such misrepair events will have no consequences to the cell and it is only for a small proportion of lethal mutations or, even more rarely, neoplasia initiating mutations that there will be clearly recognisable changes in cellular characteristics. On the basis of a direct association between DNA misrepair, somatic cell mutation and neoplastic initiation there are therefore no clearly defined mechanistic grounds for advocating a low dose threshold for the initiation of cancer by radiation. However, four major uncertainties surround this proposal. First and foremost, there is no conclusive evidence at the cellular level with which to confirm or deny the existence of such threshold effects for cancer induction. Second, it is certainly possible that the spectrum of biologically relevant induced DNA lesions changes with decreasing doses and dose rates. Third, DNA repair is not the only factor influencing the appearance of neoplasia initiated cells. Fourth, there is experimental evidence of 'adaptive responses' in some mammalian cells *in vitro* and *in vivo* whereby a low priming dose of radiation can increase resistance to a subsequent challenge by a second higher dose[40,41]; this is not, however, seen in all cellular and animal systems[42,43]. When present this response possibly involves the induction of repair proteins[40] but has yet to be shown to be associated with neoplastic initiation by radiation. In spite of these uncertainties, none of which will be easily resolved, the absence of data supporting the existence of a low dose threshold for cellular effects of radiation and the balance of evidence against this contention argue against including threshold concepts in the formulation of risk estimates at low doses.

22   There is also evidence that the lack of an effective cellular DNA repair capacity may be a determinant of the increasing effectiveness of radiation with increasing LET. DNA repair deficient mammalian cells that are highly sensitive to low LET radiations (X-rays and gamma rays) do not show the same degree of increased sensitivity to high LET neutrons and alpha particles[44]. These observations would be explained if the critical

biological damage induced by high LET radiation were inherently more difficult to repair correctly than that induced by X-rays or gamma rays, ie if the effect of high LET induced cellular damage is not substantially modified by DNA repair functions. These observations and their interpretation are also consistent with the absence of ameliorating dose rate effects for high LET radiations that have been observed in cellular systems and in carcinogenesis studies with experimental animals (Chapter 3).

GENETIC FACTORS IN HUMAN TUMORIGENESIS

23   There is increasing evidence that susceptibility to tumorigenesis is not uniform within the population and that genetic factors may influence the induction and development of a number of tumour types. The involvement of DNA metabolic processes in determining the fate of initial damage to cellular DNA and involvement of inherited mutations in tumour suppressor genes are possible mechanisms whereby human tumour susceptibility may be subject to genetic influences.

24   In the case of human homozygotes for the A-T mutation (carrying two defective DNA repair gene copies) both *in vivo* radiosensitivity and increased susceptibility to spontaneously arising lymphoreticular neoplasia are clearly evident[35]. There are, however, no data that may be used directly to link tumours in A-T homozygotes to radiation exposure; also, even if this were to be established, the frequency of A-T homozygotes in the population is too low (about 1 per 100 000 live births) to be considered as a factor in the determination of risk to the population. In contrast, while A-T heterozygotes (carrying one defective gene copy) may show only marginal cellular radiosensitivity, their estimated frequency in the population is much higher (about 1 per 100 live births) and there are reports suggestive of an increased incidence of breast cancer in obligate A-T heterozygotes[45,46]. Furthermore, preliminary data suggest the possibility that heterozygosity for the A-T gene may be associated with increased risk of radiogenic breast cancer[45] and such individuals represent one of the few human subgroups where increased susceptibility to radiation-induced cancer may be suspected. The findings of a possible association between low dose exposure and excess breast cancer in A-T heterozygotes have yet to be confirmed and have been the subject of considerable debate[47]. There are also some radiotherapy observations suggestive of increased susceptibility of Basal Cell Nevus Syndrome patients to radiation-induced skin cancer[48]. This is, however, a very rare genetic disorder but one from which it should be possible to obtain important knowledge on mechanisms of skin carcinogenesis[49].

25   At the level of initial damage to DNA there is also inconclusive evidence that the expression of heritable chromosomal 'fragile sites' that are unusually prone to breakage and rearrangement may be a factor in susceptibility to some neoplasms, particularly leukaemias. There are data that comment upon the distribution of such heritable fragile sites in the population but, as yet, the association between these and cancer susceptibility is unproven[50,51].

26   Genetic susceptibility to the childhood cancers, retinoblastoma and Wilms tumour are known to be dominantly expressing traits associated with germ line mutations affecting tumour suppressor genes. Retinoblastoma patients are also susceptible to a

range of spontaneously arising tumours and there are reports of excess secondary tumours arising in hereditary retinoblastoma patients receiving radiotherapy for primary retinal tumours[52]; these and mechanistic considerations are suggestive of increased susceptibility to radiogenic neoplasia in such cases of heritable suppressor gene loss. However, as in the case of A-T homozygotes the frequency of the known highly penetrating monogenic diseases of this type is too low to have a significant impact on the estimation of radiogenic cancer risk in the population.

27   Recently, however, data have been presented showing that genetic factors may influence susceptibility to some adult neoplasms. Rare families (Li-Fraumeni Syndrome) having certain mutations in the tumour suppressor gene, *p53*, are highly prone to the development of a range of solid tumours[53]; also, genetic loci that may determine susceptibility to a significant proportion (up to 10%) of breast cancer are now being identified[18]. While these data are as yet insufficient to be considered in the formulation of risk estimates, it may be predicted that studies in this whole area will progressively influence views on the distribution of induced cancer risk within the population. The Board believes, therefore, that consideration of individual genetic predisposition will play a significant future role in cancer risk estimation. This together with the new molecular approaches to tumour causality (paragraph 5) represent two most promising areas of fundamental study in radiological protection as related to cancer induction.

CONCLUSIONS

28   Advances in the knowledge of mechanisms of tumorigenesis may be used to support the following broad conclusions relevant to human cancer risks following exposure to ionising radiation.

(i)   Although tumorigenesis is a multistep cellular process, it has its origins (as initiating events) in single gene mutations in single target cells in tissues. On this basis there is no *a priori* biophysical basis for the existence of a low dose threshold for radiation tumorigenesis.

(ii) At low doses, radiation principally contributes to cancer risk by increasing the number of initiated cells rather than by increasing the probability that existing pre-neoplastic cells will progress to full malignancy. In general, this would tend to favour the use of multiplicative rather than additive models for risk projection with time.

(iii) Although existing evidence supports a major role for cellular DNA repair in the determination of dose rate effects, there are grounds for believing that such repair will not be totally error-free. While uncertainties remain, the repair of induced, tumour initiating DNA lesions seems unlikely to result in a low dose threshold for tumorigenic response; misrepair of DNA lesions may, however, be a major determinant of radiation quality effects.

(iv) For ionising radiation, gene loss mutations resulting in tumour initiation may be expected to be more frequent than those involving DNA base pair changes. Although still uncertain this feature may influence the relative inducibility of different tumours.

(v)   Although there is clear evidence for the influence of heritable factors on human tumour susceptibility, the existing data are not yet sufficient to be specifically considered in the formulation of risk estimates.

(vi) New molecular approaches may, in future, allow for the identification of some human tumours associated with prior exposure to radiation.

29   These conclusions should, however, be regarded as preliminary since they derive from rapidly advancing research fields where views are subject to substantial changes.

REFERENCES

1   Knudson, A G. Genetics of human cancer. *Ann. Rev. Genet.*, **20**, 231 (1986).

2   Barbacid, M. *Ras* genes. *Ann. Rev. Biochem.*, **56**, 779–878 (1987).

3   Bishop, J M. The molecular genetics of cancer. *Science*, **235**, 305 (1987).

4   Heim, S, and Mitelman, F. Primary chromosome abnormalities in human neoplasia. *Adv. Cancer Res.*, **52**, 2 (1989).

5   Sager, R. Tumour suppressor genes: The puzzle and the promise. *Science*, **246**, 1406 (1989).

6   Fearon, E R, and Vogelstein, B. A genetic model for colorectal tumorigenesis. *Cell*, **61**, 759 (1990).

7   Scrable, H J, Sapienza, C, and Cavanee, W K. Genetic and epigenetic losses of heterozygosity in cancer predisposition and progression. *Adv. Cancer Res.*, **54**, 25 (1990).

8   Weinberg, R A. Tumour suppressor genes. *Science*, **254**, 1138–46 (1991).

9   Nowell, P C. Cytogenetics of tumour progression. *Cancer*, **65**, 2172 (1990).

10   Hockenbery, D, Nunez, G, Millman, C, Schreiber, R D, and Korsmeyer, J. Bcl-2 is an inner mitochondrial membrane protein that blocks programmed cell death. *Nature*, **348**, 334–6 (1990).

11   Hatano, M, Roberts, C W M, Minden, M, Crist, W M, and Korsmeyer, J. Deregulation of a homeobox gene, *Hox* 11, by the t(10;14) in T-cell leukaemia. *Science*, **253**, 79–82 (1991).

12   Mitelman, F, Manolova, Y, Manolov, G, Billstrom, R, Heim, S, Kristoffersson, U, and Mandahl, N. High resolution analysis of the 5q- marker chromosome in refractory anaemia. *Hereditas*, **105**, 49–54 (1986).

13   Wallace, M R, Marchuk, D A, and Andersen, L B. Type 1 neurofibromatosis gene: Identification of a large transcript disrupted in three NFI patients. *Science*, **249**, 181–6 (1990).

14   Kinzler, K W, Nilbert, M C, Vogelstein, B, Bryan, T M, Levy, D B, Smith, K J, Preisinger, A C, Hamilton, S R, Hedge, P, Markham, A, Carlson, M, Joslyn, G, Groden, J, White, R, Miki, Y, Miyoshi, Y, Nishisho, I, and Nakamura, Y. Identification of a gene located at chromosome 5q21 that is mutated in colorectal cancers. *Science*, **251**, 1366–8 (1990).

15   Kinzler, K W, Nilbert, M C, Su, L-K, Vogelstein, B, Bryan, T M, Levy, D B, Smith, K J, Preisinger, A C, Hedge, P, McKechnie, D, Finniear, R, Markham, A, Groffen, J, Boguski, M S, Altschul, S F, Horii, A, Ando, H, Miyoshi, Y, Miki, Y, Nishisho, I, and Nakamura, Y. Identification of FAP locus genes from chromosome 5q21. *Science*, **253**, 661–5 (1991).

16   Nishisho, I, Nakamura, Y, Miyoshi, Y, Miki, Y, Ando, H, Horii, A, Koyama, K, Utsunomiya, J, Baba, S, Hedge, P, Maukham, A, Krush, A J, Petersen, G, Hamilton, S R, Nilbert, M C, Levy, D B, Bryan, T M, Preisinger, A C, Smith, K J, Su, L-K, Kinzler, K W, and Vogelstein, B. Mutations of chromosome 5q21 genes in FAP and colorectal cancer patients. *Science*, **253**, 665–9 (1991).

17   Hollstein, M, Sidransky, D, Vogelstein, B, and Harris, C C. *p53* mutations in human cancers. *Science*, **253**, 49–53 (1991).

18   Hall, J M, Lee, M K, Newman, B, Morrow, J E, Anderson, J E, Huey, B, and King, M C. Linkage of early onset familial breast cancer to chromosome 17q21. *Science*, **250**, 1684–9 (1990).

19   Hsu, I C, Metcalf, R A, Sun, T, Welsh, J A, Wang, N J, and Harris, C C. Mutational hotspot in the *p53* gene in human hepatocellular carcinomas. *Nature*, **350**, 427–8 (1991).

20   Bressac, B, Kew, M, Wands, J, and Ozturk, M. Selective G to T mutations of *p53* gene in hepatocellular carcinoma from southern Africa. *Nature*, **350**, 429–31 (1991).

21   Ozturk, M, *et al. p53* mutation in hepatocellular carcinoma after aflatoxin exposure. *Lancet*, **338**, 1356–9 (1991).

22   Brash, D E, Rudolf, J A, Simon, J A, Lin, A, McKenna, G J, Baden, H P, Halperin, A J, and Poten, J. A role for sunlight in skin cancer: UV-induced *p53* mutations in squamous cell carcinoma. *Proc. Natl Acad. Sci. (USA),* **88**, 10124–8 (1991).

23   Vahakangas, K H, Samet, J M, Metcalf, R A, Welsh, J A, Bennett, W P, Lane, D P, and Harris, C C. Mutations of *p53* and *ras* genes in radon-associated lung cancer from uranium miners. *Lancet,* **339**, 576–80 (1992).

24   Harris, C C. Chemical and physical carcinogenesis: Advances and perspectives for the 1990s. *Cancer Res.* (**Suppl.**), **51**, 5023s–44s (1991).

25   Yuspa, S H, and Poireier, M C. Chemical carcinogenesis from animal models to molecular models in one decade. *Adv. Cancer Res.,* **50**, 25–70 (1988).

26   Trosko, J E, Chang, C C, Madhukar, B V, and Klaunig, J E. Chemical, oncogene and growth factor inhibition of gap junction intercellular communication: An integrative hypothesis of carcinogenesis. *Pathobiology,* **58**, 265–78 (1990).

27   Foulds, L. *Neoplastic Development,* Volume 2. New York, Academic Press (1975).

28   Hart, I R, Goode, N T, and Wilson, R E. Molecular aspects of the metastatic cascade. *Biochim. Biophys. Acta,* **989**, 65–84 (1989).

29   Sankaranarayanan, K. Ionising radiation and genetic risks III. Nature of spontaneous and radiation induced mutations in mammalian *in vitro* systems and mechanisms of mutation by radiation. *Mutation Res.,* **258**, 75–97 (1991).

30   Land, C E, and Sinclair, W K. The relative contributions of different organ sites to the total cancer mortality associated with low-dose radiation exposure. *Ann. ICRP,* **22**, 31–57 (1991).

31   Kumar, R, Sukumar, S, and Barbacid, M. Activation of *ras* oncogenes preceding the onset of neoplasia. *Science,* **248**, 1101–4 (1990).

32   Greaves, M F. Speculations on the cause of childhood acute lymphoblastic leukaemia. *Leukaemia,* **2**, 120–25 (1988).

33   Reik, W. Genomic imprinting and genetic disorders in man. *Trends Genet.,* **5**, 331–6 (1989).

34   Frieberg, E C, and Hanawalt, P C (eds). *Mechanisms and Consequences of DNA Damage Processing.* New York, A R Liss (1988).

35   Bridges, B A, and Harnden, D G (eds). *Ataxia Telangiectasia.* Chichester, John Wiley (1982).

36   Little, J B, and Nove, J. Sensitivity of human diploid fibroblast cell strains from various genetic disorders to acute and protracted radiation exposure. *Radiat. Res.,* **123**, 87–92 (1990).

37   Debenham, P G, Webb, M, Jones, N, Masson, W, and Cox, R. Molecular studies on the nature of the repair defect in ataxia telangiectasia and their implications for cellular radiobiology. *J. Cell Sci.* (**Suppl. 6**), 1977–83 (1987).

38   Thacker, J. Inherited sensitivity to x-rays in man. *BioEssays,* **11**, 58–62 (1989).

39   Thacker, J. Radiation-induced mutation in mammalian cells at low doses and low dose rates. *Adv. Radiat. Biol.,* **16**, 77–117 (1992).

40   Wolff, S, Wiencke, J K, Afzal, V, Youngbloom, J, and Cortes, F. The adaptive response of human lymphocytes to very low doses of ionizing radiation: A case of induced chromosomal repair with the induction of specific proteins. IN *Low Dose Radiation: Biological Bases of Risk Assessment* (K F Baverstock and J W Stather, eds). London, Taylor and Francis, pp 446–54 (1989).

41   Liu, S Z, Cai, L, and Sun, S Q. Induction of a cytogenetic adaptive response by exposure of rabbits to very low dose-rate γ-radiation. *Int. J. Radiat. Biol.,* **62**, 187–90 (1992).

42   Wojcik, A, Bouk, K, Muller, W-U, Streffer, C, Weissenborn, U, and Obe, G. Absence of adaptive response to low doses of X-rays in preimplantation embryos and spleen lymphocytes of an inbred mouse strain as compared to human peripheral lymphocytes: A cytogenetic study. *Int. J. Radiat. Biol.,* **62**, 177–86 (1992).

43   Muller, W-U, Streffer, C, and Niedereichholz, F. Adaptive response in mouse embryos? *Int. J. Radiat. Biol.,* **62**, 169–75 (1992).

44   Cox, R. A cellular description of the repair defect in ataxia telangiectasia. IN *Ataxia Telangiectasia* (B A Bridges and D G Harnden, eds). Chichester, John Wiley, pp 141–53 (1982).

45   Swift, M, Reitnauer, P J, Morrell, D, and Chase, C L. Breast and other cancers in families with ataxia telangiectasia. *N. Engl. J. Med.,* **316**, 1289–94 (1987).

46   Pippard, E C, Hall, A J, Barker, D J, and Bridges, B A. Cancer in homozygotes and heterozygotes of ataxia telangiectasia and xeroderma pigmentosum in Britain. *Cancer Res.,* **48**, 2929–32 (1988).

47   Correspondence. *N. Engl. J. Med.*, **326**, 1357–61 (1992).

48   Strong, L. Genetic and environmental interactions. *Cancer*, **40**, 1861–6 (1977).

49   Newton, J A, Kobza Black, A, Arlett, C F, and Cole, J. Radiobiological studies in the naevoid basal cell carcinoma syndrome. *Br. J. Dermatol.*, **123**, 573–80 (1990).

50   Sutherland, G R, and Simmers, R N. No statistical association between common fragile sites and non-random chromosome breakpoints in cancer cells. *Cancer Genet. Cytogenet.*, **31**, 9 (1988).

51   Le Beau, M M. Chromosome fragile sites and cancer specific breakpoints – A moderating viewpoint. *Cancer Genet. Cytogenet.*, **31**, 55 (1988).

52   Draper, G J, Sanders, B M, and Kingston, J E. Second primary neoplasms in patients with retinoblastoma. *Br. J. Cancer*, **53**, 661–71 (1986).

53   Srivastava, S, Zou, Z, Pirollo, K, Blattner, W, and Chang, E H. Germ line transmission of a mutated *p53* gene in a cancer-prone family with Li-Fraumeni syndrome. *Nature*, **348**, 747 (1990).

3 Effect of Dose and Dose Rate on Radiation-induced Cancer and Hereditary Disease

INTRODUCTION

1   Quantitative information on the risk of cancer in human populations exposed to ionising radiation comes largely from information available from groups exposed at intermediate and high doses and dose rates. For radiation protection purposes, however, the assessment of risk from environmental and occupational exposure to radiation must be determined for exposures to low doses delivered at low dose rates. Information is therefore needed on the extent to which both total dose and dose rate influence cancer induction in exposed individuals. Information is also required on the effect of dose rate on radiation-induced hereditary disease. The designation of low doses and low dose rates is described in Chapter 8.

CANCER INDUCTION

2   The two features of the dose response that are most important for evaluation of the cancer risk at low doses are the possible presence of a threshold dose, below which no effect would exist, and the shape of the dose response.

3   For most tumour types, however, proving or disproving a threshold is likely to be impossible, due to statistical uncertainties in both the spontaneous and induced incidences of the disease. Therefore, on the assumption that specific cellular targets can be altered by single tracks, that repair may not be error-free, and the possibility that the resulting damage may ultimately give rise to a tumour (Chapter 2) it is normally assumed that there is no threshold for tumour induction. This working hypothesis is consistent with many observations of induced cancer rates found in animal experiments and observed in epidemiological studies.

4   Studies at the molecular, cellular, tissue and whole animal level have demonstrated that radiation damage increases with dose and that, at least for low LET radiation, at high dose rates it is often greater per unit of exposure than at low dose rates. Although the assumption normally made for radiation protection purposes is that the dose–response curve for cancer induction is linear, with the risk proportional to dose, in practice a dose and dose rate effectiveness factor (DDREF) has commonly been used to allow for a reduced effectiveness of radiation in inducing cancer in man at low doses and low dose rates[1]. The terms dose rate effectiveness factor (DREF)[2] and linear extrapolation overestimation factor (LEOF)[3,4] have also been used. Recent estimates of DDREF by a number of organisations are given in Table 3.1.

5   A full understanding of the mechanisms involved in tumour initiation, promotion and progression (Chapter 2) will be necessary to understand how dose and dose rate affect tumour induction. Until this information is available, considerable reliance must be placed upon the limited information from epidemiological studies, together with results available from studies in experimental animals and on cells in culture.

Source	DDREF	Year	Reference
International Commission on Radiological Protection (ICRP)	2 2	1977 1991	5 1
National Council on Radiation Protection and Measurements (NCRP)	2–10	1980	2
National Radiological Protection Board (NRPB)	3*	1988	6
United Nations Scientific Committee on the Effects of Atomic Radiation (UNSCEAR)	2.5 Up to 5 2–10	1977 1986 1988	7 8 9
United States Nuclear Regulatory Commission (USNRC)	3.3 2	1989 1991	10 11
National Radiological Protection Board (NRPB)	2	1993	This report

*2 for breast.

DOSE–RESPONSE RELATIONSHIPS

6   Guidance as to likely dose and dose rate effects on tumour response may be obtained from radiobiological data on other cellular effects which result from DNA damage as well as from studies on tumour induction in experimental animals and from epidemiological studies. It needs to be recognised, however, that cellular data are mostly for single-stage radiation effects and therefore represent only a part of the complex carcinogenesis process.

7   In the 1986 UNSCEAR report[8] information on dose–response relationships for mutations, for chromosomal aberrations in mammalian cells, for cell transformation and for radiation-induced cancer were reviewed. Three basic non-threshold models were considered with respect both to cellular effects of radiation and to cancer induction: the linear, the linear–quadratic and the pure quadratic models. It was concluded that for the bulk of experiments and many endpoints the prevailing form of the dose–response relationship at intermediate to high doses of low LET radiation is concave upward, and the induction, I, of an effect at dose, D, can be represented by an equation of general approximation with the form:

$$I(D) = (\alpha_1 D + \alpha_2 D^2)e^{-(\beta_1 D + \beta_2 D^2)}$$

where α_1 and α_2 are coefficients for the linear and quadratic terms for the specific response and β_1 and β_2 represent linear and quadratic terms for cell inactivation or killing. At low doses, tumour response (or other cellular damage) is determined by α_1 with the response increasing linearly with dose. It is generally assumed that in this region α_1 will be independent of dose rate. With increasing dose the amount of damage due to multiple tracks increases, resulting in a dose–response curve that can be fitted by a linear–quadratic function. At doses above a few gray β_1 and β_2 become significant, resulting in a reduction in tumour yield due to the effect of cell killing. This biophysical model has been challenged in recent years, largely on the basis of data with soft X-rays, which are highly effective biologically even though the length of the secondary tracks they produce is too short to enable a single track to break two independent chromosomes[12]. An alternative model has been proposed in which biological damage is presumed to result from single track effects, with the additional factor of a repair process that saturates at higher doses (see also Chapter 2). It should be noted that those models are not mutually exclusive.

8   For mammalian cells which show a dose response that can be fitted by a linear–quadratic function, radiosensitivity is generally described in terms of the α_1/α_2 ratio which gives the dose at which the two terms contribute equally to the dose response, in the absence of cell killing effects. Thus for cells in which the ratio is large ($\alpha_1/\alpha_2 > 2.0$ Gy) this implies that the linear term predominates at low doses (< 2 Gy), whereas where the ratio is small ($\alpha_1/\alpha_2 < 0.5$ Gy) the quadratic term is important even at low doses. This linear–quadratic model fit to experimental data can be used to demonstrate how the range of values of the parameters will affect the shape of the dose–response curve for a given radiation effect, and the extent of overestimation of the effect at low doses by linear extrapolation from risks obtained at intermediate or high doses. The maximum overestimation of the risk (DDREF) results from totally neglecting cell killing. In such a case the DDREF is given by

$$\text{DDREF} = \frac{\alpha_1 D + \alpha_2 D^2}{\alpha_1 D} = 1 + \frac{\alpha_2}{\alpha_1} D$$

Linear extrapolation from 3, 2 and 1 Gy down to a low dose of, say, 0.01 Gy would thus involve an overestimation of the effect by a factor which depends not only on the dose but also on the ratio α_1/α_2. Calculated factors are tabulated below.

Ratio α_1/α_2 (Gy)	DDREF		
	3 Gy	2 Gy	1 Gy
0.5	7	5	3
1.0	4	3	2
2.0	2.5	2	1.5

Thus, for a cell response with an α_1/α_2 ratio of 1.0 Gy, if the risk is assessed at 2 Gy then linear extrapolation to assess the risk at low doses will overestimate the risk coefficient by a factor of 3. If the risk is assessed at 3 Gy, however, then the DDREF would be 4.

9   The problems in assessing risks of cancer for exposures to low LET radiation at low doses and low dose rates, when human data are available mainly at high doses and high dose rates, were summarised by NCRP[2] and are illustrated in Figure 3.1. This schematic plot gives data points and possible dose–response curves for cancer induction by low LET radiation. Frequently, as in this example, data points are only available at relatively high doses. The approach commonly used in risk assessment is to fit a linear

dose–response relationship to the data (curve B), a procedure that is usually considered to give an upper limit to the risk at low doses[5,7,13,14]. If this linear relationship is due to single events which do not interact, then the effect per unit dose (the slope of the line α_H or risk coefficient at high doses) would be expected to be independent of dose magnitude and dose rate. In practice, however, this is not generally the case, and experimental data suggest that a linear–quadratic relationship (curve A) will frequently provide a better fit to the data at low to intermediate doses, implying that damage is the result of both single events and other more complex interactions. With a progressive lowering of the dose and the dose rate, allowing more opportunity for repair of damage and less opportunity for interacting events, a point may ultimately be reached at which damage is produced only as a result of single events acting alone, giving a linear response (curve D, slope α_L) with the effect proportional to dose. A similar response would be obtained by lowering the dose rate alone as, even at high total doses, the rate of accumulation of lesions is slower. Thus, experimentally the effect per unit absorbed dose at low dose rates (even at high total doses), would be expected to become progressively less as the dose rate is lowered. Hence, the limiting slope (α_L of Figure 3.1) would be reached either by reducing the dose to very low values where the response is independent of dose rate or by reducing the dose rate to very low values where the effect is dependent only on the total dose.

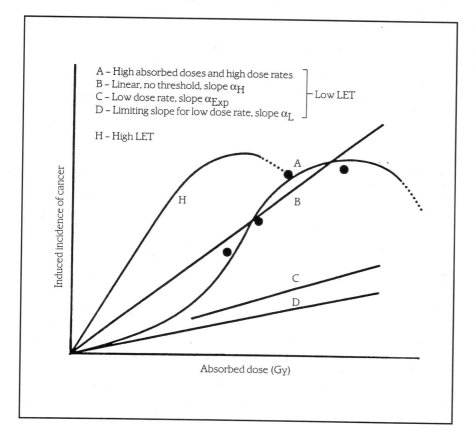

FIGURE 3.1
Dose–response relationship for radiation–induced cancer

10   The ratio of the slope α_H of the no-threshold 'apparently' linear fit to the high dose and high dose rate data to the slope α_L of the linear curve for the low dose rate data is an estimate of the dose and dose rate effectiveness factor (DDREF).

11   In practice, it is extremely difficult to detect radiation-induced effects in the low dose region (< 0.1 Gy), at any dose rate, thus there are uncertainties in the determination of the limiting slope α_L. The initial slope of the dose–response curve can be more readily examined by changing the dose rate, as may be done in studies with experimental animals. In many experiments, even at low or intermediate dose rates, the limiting slope may not, however, be reached and a dose response in between the two slopes α_H and α_L is obtained with slope α_{Exp}. Despite this limitation, animal experiments provide the best indication of the extent to which lowering the dose rate of low LET radiation, even at intermediate or high total doses, can reduce the effectiveness of radiation in inducing cancer.

TUMOUR INDUCTION IN EXPERIMENTAL ANIMALS

12   Radiation-induced life shortening in experimental animals is mainly the result of an increase in tumour incidence[8], with little suggestion of a general increase in other causes of death, although degenerative diseases in some tissues may be increased at high doses. On this basis, life shortening can be used to assess the effect of dose fractionation and protraction on tumour induction.

13   Data on the induction of specific tumours in experimental animals are most directly useful for the derivation of DDREFs for man but are unfortunately restricted in their extent. Significant effects have been obtained mainly with relatively high doses (> 0.2 Gy, low LET) although at very different dose rates. Thus, only limited evaluation of the overall dose response has been achieved[8]. Data are also available on fractionated exposures.

Low LET radiation

14   The majority of comprehensive studies on the effect of fractionation of low LET radiation on lifespan has been undertaken using the mouse as the experimental animal, with the effects observed being very dependent on the strain and the spectrum of diseases contributing to the overall death rate. Overall there is no clear trend and the results from a number of studies suggest that, when compared with acute exposures, the effects of fractionation on lifespan are small and, at least for exposure times of about a month, simple additivity of the injury from each dose increment can be assumed. For fractionation intervals over a longer period of time there is a tendency to a longer lifespan with an increasing interval between the doses but the variations observed are generally less than those found with protracted exposures[8].

15   When the effects of acute exposures to low LET radiation are compared with protracted irradiation given more or less continuously, there is a trend of decreasing effectiveness of the radiation with decreasing dose rate and increasing time of exposure[2] with similar results obtained in a number of strains of mice[15]. For lifetime exposures, however, there is some difficulty assessing the total dose contributing to the loss of lifespan. With protracted exposures over a period of a few months to a year the effective lifespan shortening in mice is reduced by factors between about two and five

compared with acute exposures[2]. Thomson and Grahn[16] have recently compared life-shortening coefficients for mice given single, fractionated and continuous cobalt-60 gamma exposures (Table 3.2). The maximum reduction in effect was found by comparing single acute exposure with the effect of continuous exposure over 59 weeks, when the reduction in effectiveness is about a factor of five. However, with prolonged exposure there will be some dose which will not have contributed to tumour induction and the loss of lifespan. For comparing different patterns of exposure it may, therefore, be more appropriate to compare the effect of continuous and fractionated exposures given over the same period of time. On this basis a DDREF in the range 1.4–2.3 is obtained from the results in Table 3.2.

Type of exposure	Time pattern	Coefficient of life shortening (days lost per Gy)	Reference
Single	–	38.5 ± 2.9	17
Fractionated	24 once per week	22.6 ± 2.9	17
	60 once per week	17.5 ± 3.3	18
Continuous	For 23 weeks	15.8 ± 2.2	16
	For 59 weeks	7.7 ± 0.2	16

TABLE 3.2
Life shortening from single, fractionated and continuous gamma ray exposure of mice[16]

16   A number of studies have been published which permit the effect of dose rate on tumour induction in experimental animals to be examined. The data that have been reported by various authors cover a wide range of dose–response relationships, and the assessment of the extent to which changing the dose rate alters the effectiveness of the radiation depends on the dose range over which DDREFs are calculated. The results of the main studies that have been published are summarised in Table 3.3. A wide range of DDREFs for tumour induction in a variety of different tissues has been found. Some of the tumour types for which information is available are not found in man (Harderian gland, thymic lymphoma) or appear to involve substantial cell killing and/or changes in hormonal status for them to develop (ovarian tumour, thymic lymphoma). For others there is a human counterpart (myeloid leukaemia and tumours of the lung, mammary tissues, pituitary and thyroid glands), although the tumours involved may not be strictly comparable to the human disease. In practice, the DDREFs found in these two groups are little different, falling in the range from about 1 to 10 or more. Furthermore, there is no clear trend with tissue type. Thus, data on myeloid leukaemia induction in different species and sexes of mice have been reported which span the range of DDREFs from about 2 to > 10. The one reasonably consistent finding is that DDREFs for tumour induction in mammary tissue tend to be lower than for other tissues, although even here a substantial effect of dose fractionation on the tumour response in mice has been reported[31].

17   A number of the animal studies also indicate that the presence of a dose rate effect could not necessarily be inferred from exposures at high dose rates alone as the dose–response data at low to intermediate doses could be adequately fitted by a linear function. A departure from linearity in the dose response is necessary for an effect of

TABLE 3.3 *Dose and dose rate effectiveness factors (DDREF) for tumour induction in experimental animals*

Effects	Animal studied	Dose rate (mGy min⁻¹) High	Dose rate (mGy min⁻¹) Low	DDREF	References
Myeloid leukaemia	CBA/H male mice	250	0.04–0.11	2.2–5	19
	RFM male mice	800	0.04–0.6	5.1	20
	RFM/Un female mice	450	0.06	9.7–∞	21
	RF female mice	67	0.004–0.7	~8	20
Lung adenocarcinomas	BALB/c mice	400	0.06	2.8	21,22
Lung cancer[a]	Beagle dogs			~3	23
Mammary tumours	BALB/c mice	450	0.06	1.9	22
	Sprague-Dawley rats	10–30	0.02–0.14	1.6–1.7	24
	Sprague-Dawley rats	100	0.3	~1	25
	WAG/RIJ rats[b]	2 Gy	(2 Gy)[b]	~1	26
Mammary adenocarcinomas	Sprague-Dawley rats	100	0.3	4	25
Pituitary tumours	BALB/c mice	450	0.06	~6	21,27
Thyroid tumours[c]	CBA mice	(15 Gy)	(64–160 Gy)	2–10	28
	Rats	(11 Gy)	(100 Gy)	~10	29
	Long Evans rats	2800	(0.08–8.5 Gy)	~1	30
Harderian gland tumours	RFM female mice	450	0.06	~3	21,22,27
Ovarian tumours	RFM mice	450	0.06	~5.5	21
	RFM mice	400	0.06	6.7	
Thymic lymphoma	RFM female mice	450	0.06	5.8	21,22
	RFM male mice	800	0.04–0.6	2.6	20

Notes
(a) High dose rate from ⁹¹Y; low dose rate from ¹⁴⁴Ce or ⁹⁰Sr. (b) Ten fractions of 0.2 Gy each versus single exposure. (c) High dose rate from X-rays; low dose rate from ¹³¹I.

dose rate on tumour yield. It is thus clear that where information is available only for exposures at high dose rates, any assessment of a dose rate effect by attempting to fit a linear–quadratic function to the dose response may be inadequate. The limiting factor is the amount of information available at low doses from which the initial linear term can be accurately defined.

18   The main conclusions to be drawn from the results available from both the studies on radiation-induced life shortening and those on induction of specific tumour types is that for low LET radiation tumour induction is generally reduced at low dose rates compared with high dose rates. While the absolute value of the DDREF varies with the conditions of exposure, the animal strain, tissue/tumour type and the dose range over which it is calculated, there is in general a consistent finding of a reduction in tumour yield with a reduction in the dose rate.

High LET radiation

19   For exposure to high LET radiation most recent studies have shown that when total doses are low and the dose per fraction is small, there is no significant difference in life shortening between fractionated and acute exposures[32-36]. The implication of these results is that fractionation should have little effect on tumour induction, as this is the main cause of lifespan shortening. Grahn and Carnes[37] have examined the main categories of cancers found in B6CF1 mice following acute and fractionated exposures; namely, those of lymphoid and epithelial tissues. The results obtained so far indicate that the mortality from lymphoma and leukaemia is greater after fractionated exposures than single exposures, whereas mortality from epithelial tumours is lower with the fractionated than single exposures. Since no fractionation effect is seen on the overall lifespan in the dose range up to 0.2 Gy it has to be assumed that the two effects cancel each other out, although suggesting effects of fractionation on individual tumour types.

20   Other reported effects of protracted and fractionated neutron irradiation on the induction of tumours give variable results in different tissues and have recently been reviewed by Fry[38]. Upton *et al*[20] did not find any difference in the effects of protracted neutron exposures at low dose rates on the induction of myeloid leukaemia in RFM mice compared with that obtained after single doses. Protraction of exposure to neutron irradiation increased the incidence of mammary tumours in mice[39] and advanced the time of appearance of mammary tumours in rats[40] more than single exposures. Exposures to fractions of 25 mGy up to a total dose of 0.4 Gy were no more effective than single doses for the induction of tumours of Harderian glands[41].

21   Recently, Huiskamp *et al*[42] reported no effect of dose rate on either the induction of myeloid leukaemia or survival time in male CBA/H mice exposed to fast fission neutrons at 2, 10 and 100 mGy min^{-1} to give a total dose of 0.4 Gy. The results did suggest a small increase in lymphosarcoma in the high dose rate group, although numbers were small and with no clear trend with increasing dose rate.

22   Some information is also available for tumour induction in experimental animals following intake of alpha emitting radionuclides. The interpretation of such data is, however, considerably more difficult than is the case for neutron exposure. The spatial and temporal distribution of dose throughout a tissue will depend on the age of the animal and the pattern of intake as well as the radionuclide and the chemical form in which it enters the body. Thus, even for the same radionuclide given in the same

chemical form the distribution of dose may be very different after acute and protracted exposures, and this is likely to affect the tumour yield. The published data have recently been summarised[43].

23   A number of studies suggest that at low dose rates alpha particle irradiation is more effective at inducing tumours per unit of dose than when exposures are at high dose rates[44-49]. However, this type of response tends to occur at high total doses and the difference in effect could be attributed to cell killing.

24   From the limited animal data available it is difficult to generalise but there is little experimental support for applying a DDREF to high dose and high dose rate exposures from high LET radiation to calculate risks at low doses and low dose rates. There is also little evidence to suggest that, in the absence of cell killing, there is an appreciable increase in tumour induction when the dose from high LET radiation is protracted or fractionated.

CELL TRANSFORMATION

25   Transformation studies on cells in culture have been used to provide additional data on dose rate effects. To date, however, the only quantitative data have been derived from cultured embryo cells or the mouse fibroblast cell lines C3H10T$^{1/2}$ and BALB/c3T3 which are not typical of tumour cell types in man, many of which arise in epithelial tissues. Thus, when attempting to extrapolate to cancer induction in man, the biological limitations of these assay systems must be considered. In addition, a number of technical uncertainties which include the effects of cell cycle time, plating density and of promoters and suppressors, some of which may be normal components of the growth medium, are difficult to control and thereby make full evaluation of the data somewhat problematical.

Low LET radiation

26   Despite the limitation of the cell transformation assays described above, in carefully controlled experiments where asynchronously dividing cells or, in some cases, non-dividing plateau phase cells have been irradiated, the resulting observations on dose or dose rate effects for low LET radiation are in general agreement with those relating to other cellular effects, such as cell killing, induction of mutations or chromosomal aberrations and tumour induction in animals. Dose–response curves per cell at risk have a number of features in common with tumour induction *in vivo*, showing an initial rise in transformation frequency with increasing dose to a maximum and then a decline. When plotted as transformations per surviving cell, the dose response for low LET radiation generally shows the expected linear or linear–quadratic relationship tailing off to a plateau at higher doses. When low doses of X-rays or gamma rays are delivered at low dose rate or in fractionated intervals, a DDREF of between two and four has been found[50-52]. It is noteworthy that some experimental data suggest that the linear term may alter with dose rate although this may possibly be accounted for by the lack of precise data at low doses[50]. It is possible that a dose rate at which the effects are dependent only on total dose and not dose rate was not used.

High LET radiation

27   Exposure to high LET radiation results in a higher transformation efficiency than for low LET radiation with a tendency towards a linear dose–response relationship, with no

tendency to decrease the effect at low dose rates or with fractionation. In practice, a number of studies have shown an enhanced effect at low dose rates. The main experimental evidence for a so-called 'inverse' dose rate effect with high LET radiation seems to be limited to 5.9 MeV or fission spectrum neutrons[53]. Over the past few years estimates of the magnitude of the increased effect have been reduced[54] from factors of around nine to about two or three. Results reported from a number of laboratories have become reasonably consistent, and it has been possible to develop a model that can satisfactorily predict most experimental results. The model is based on the assumption that the target in the cell, taken to be the nucleus, has a 'window' in the cell cycle in which it is more sensitive to radiation[55,56].

28   With protracted or fractionated exposures there is a greater opportunity for this particular 'window' to be hit, and thus the possibility for an enhancement of transformation frequency with a reduction in dose rate. The magnitude of any effect will depend on the lineal energy, and with alpha particle irradiation little enhancement would be expected, as is in fact observed. Although such a model appears to be consistent with much of the experimental data it is very dependent on the target size and it will need to be tested at different doses, dose rates and fractionation schedules for a full examination of its general applicability. Other explanations are also possible.

29   Despite this apparent explanation for the inverse dose rate effect there remains the problem that it is largely based on the results obtained with the C3H10T½ cell system and may well only have limited applications to human carcinogenesis. The development of epithelial cell systems that are of much more direct relevance to human cancer is a priority[57].

MUTAGENESIS IN SOMATIC CELLS

30   It is generally believed that the principal mechanism resulting in a neoplastic initiating event is induced damage to the DNA molecule which predisposes target cells to subsequent malignant development (Chapter 2). There is also strong evidence linking a number of tumours to specific gene mutations. There is therefore a need to understand the role of both dose and dose rate in this initial genetic change. The effect of dose and dose rate on radiation-induced mutation in somatic cells has been reviewed by Thacker[58].

31   A number of mutation systems have been described in the literature, but only a few are sufficiently well defined for quantitative studies. Mutation of a single gene is a relatively rare event; most experimental systems are therefore designed to select out cells carrying mutations. Commonly used systems employ the loss of function of a gene product (enzyme) which is not essential for the survival of cells in culture. Thus cells may be challenged with a toxic drug that they would normally metabolise with fatal consequences. If mutation renders the gene producing the specific enzyme ineffective, the cell will survive, and thus the mutation frequency can be obtained by measuring the survivors. A frequently used example of such a system is that employing the loss of the enzyme hypoxanthine-guanine phosphoribosyl transferase (HPRT), which renders cells resistant to the drug 6-thioguanine (6-TG), and of the enzyme thymidine kinase (TK) giving resistance to trifluorthymidine (TFT). HPRT-activity is

specified by an X-linked gene (hprt), while TK is specified by an autosomal gene (tk) and therefore has to be used in the heterozygous state.

32   There are a number of difficulties with such somatic cell systems, and these were reviewed by Thacker[58]. In particular, the mutation frequency of a given gene is to some extent modifiable depending on the exact conditions of the experiment. There may also be a period of time that is needed for the mutation to manifest itself. Thus the true mutation frequency may be difficult to determine, and this can present particular difficulties in studies of the effect of dose rate when exposures can be spread over varying periods of time.

33   Several established cell lines, derived from mouse, hamster or human tissue, have been used to measure mutant frequencies at different dose rates. The cells lines used experimentally can have sensitivities which depend on the stage of the cell cycle, and thus to ensure as consistent a response as possible, it is preferable to use a stationary culture in plateau phase in which only a limited number of the cells will be cycling in the confluent monolayer[59,60]. The range of published data on the effect of dose rate on mutant frequency encompasses both a lack of effect to a marked effect with values of DDREF up to about three (see, for example, references 61–63). The results obtained in different cell lines have also demonstrated significant influences on the effect of gamma rays on cell growth taking place during protracted irradiation, (see, for example, references 11, 63 and 64).

EPIDEMIOLOGY

34   The epidemiological data available for assessing the effects of radiation on tumour induction at low doses are very limited although some data are available. Thus the most recent data[65,66] on the survivors of the atomic bombings in Japan have demonstrated a significant increase in the risk of solid cancers in the dose range 0.2–0.5 Gy; in a study by Shore *et al*[67], excess thyroid cancers have been observed at a mean dose of 0.17 Gy; an excess of thyroid cancer[68] was also seen among Israeli children with ringworm of the scalp receiving a mean dose of 0.09 Gy; for *in utero* irradiation an excess cancer risk in the first 15 years of life has been obtained following doses of about 0.01 Gy, in the Oxford Survey of Childhood Cancer[69,70].

35   The main source of information on dose–response relationships for human exposure to radiation comes from the population of atomic bomb survivors in Japan with reported follow-up data to 1985. Pierce and Vaeth[3,4] concluded, on the basis of an analysis of the data over the range 0–4 Gy kerma (adjusted for random errors) that a point estimate of the low dose extrapolation factor (ie DDREF) of 1.7 (90% confidence interval (CI) 1.1–3.1) could be inferred from the data for all cancers combined (with adjustment for random errors in dose estimates). For leukaemia alone the DDREF was calculated to be 1.95 (90% CI 1.1 to at least 3.1). They emphasised that the use of DDREFs much above 2 would need to be based on information from experimental studies and that their interpretation depends strongly on the assumption that a linear–quadratic model is appropriate for extrapolation to low doses (Chapter 4).

36   For thyroid cancer induction, dose–response data following acute exposures of children can be fitted by a linear dose response[67], whereas comparative data on thyroid tumour induction following exposure to external radiation and to internally incorporated iodine-131 suggest a DDREF of at least 3, although other factors such as the distribution of dose may also be important[71-73]. A relatively low value of the dose rate effectiveness factor is also suggested from human data on breast cancer, where dose–response data at high dose rates appear linear and with no effect of fractionation[8]. Some recently published data on breast cancer induction following fluoroscopic examination obtained in follow-up studies in Nova Scotia compared with other provinces in Canada[74] suggest a DDREF of about 3, although interpretation of the data presents difficulties and the relative risks for the low dose rate group in the other provinces is similar to that found in the atomic bomb survivors, exposed at high dose rate (see Chapter 4).

37   Information is also becoming available from epidemiological studies on groups exposed at low dose rates. The most important of these are studies on workers who have been occupationally exposed but there are also studies on people exposed to weapons fallout in Southern Utah and groups in areas of high background radiation. The topic of low dose rate studies is considered in Appendix B. Some of these studies, particularly the UK National Registry for Radiation Workers study[75], provide indications of excess risks but the statistical uncertainties are large (see also Chapter 4). However, they can be seen as supporting the use of a low value for DDREF. The effect of dose rate on lung tumour induction in miners exposed to radon and its decay products is also considered in Chapter 4.

GERM CELL MUTATIONS

38   The effect of dose rate on the induction of specific locus mutations in rodents has been reviewed elsewhere[2,76,77]. Mutation studies on mouse spermatogonia provided the first unambiguous demonstration of a dose rate effect for mutational changes other than cytologically recognised gross chromosomal aberrations[78]. No dose rate effects have been demonstrated for mutations induced in mature sperm as they are devoid of cytoplasm and have relatively low metabolic activity. As a consequence, there is no opportunity for repair processes to operate and thus for dose rate influences to be effective. Unlike the mature sperm, spermatogonial cells are metabolically active and repair processes can modify the yield of mutations or chromosomal aberrations with protracted irradiation. On protraction of low LET radiation the yield of mutations per gray in mouse spermatogonia decreases by a factor of about three as the dose rate is reduced from roughly 800–900 mGy min^{-1} to 8 mGy min^{-1} (11.5 Gy d^{-1}). Further reduction of the dose rate to 0.007 mGy min^{-1} (10 mGy d^{-1}) failed to lower the yield further[77,79]. As this independence of dose rate had been shown over a range of more than 1000-fold it was concluded that it was unlikely that a further reduction in mutation frequency at even lower dose rates would be obtained. The mutation frequency obtained at dose rates from 720 to 900 mGy min^{-1}, with total doses up to about 6 Gy, was compared with that obtained at low dose rates[77], on the basis of linear fits to the data, to give a DDREF of 3.0 ± 0.41. Similar results have been reported by Lyon *et al*[80]. Information on dose rate effects in female mice are less clear, although dose rate effects have been observed[81].

39   The observation of a DDREF of 3 for damage to spermatogonia has been applied by UNSCEAR since 1972[82] in assessing risks of hereditary disease for both sexes at low dose rates. In its most recent report[9] a DDREF of 3 is still applied.

CONCLUSIONS

40   The results of studies in experimental animals conducted over a somewhat higher dose range from that at which the Japanese atomic bomb survivors were exposed give dose and dose rate effectiveness factors (DDREFs) in the range from about 1 to more than 10. Similar results have been obtained for transformation of cells in culture and for somatic cell mutations where DDREFs up to about 3 have been obtained. Many of these experimental studies compared widely different dose rates, and in a number of these linear functions would give a good fit to both the high and low dose rate data in the range from low to intermediate doses. This indicates that if the cellular response can, in principle, be fitted by a linear–quadratic dose response, in practice it is not always possible to resolve the common linear term for exposures at different dose rates. If the human response is similar to that in experimental animals, then it can be envisaged that at lower dose rates than were experienced in the atomic bombings in Japan, a dose rate effectiveness factor greater than that obtained from the data on the atomic bomb survivors in Japan (ie > 1.5) could be obtained. However, information from human populations exposed at low dose rates suggests that risk coefficients are not appreciably different from those obtained for the atomic bomb survivors (exposed at high dose rates) although the uncertainty in the low dose rate studies are fairly large. Taken together, the available human and animal data suggest that it would be appropriate to apply a low value of DDREF and a value of 2 is adopted here for all tissues as there are insufficient data to justify recommending different values for different tissues. In previous Board advice[6] a DDREF of 3 was recommended for all cancers except breast, for which a DDREF of 2 was used. This advice was based mainly on the results from experimental studies.

41   There is no clear experimental support for applying a DDREF to exposures from high LET radiation, although departures from linear dose–response curves have been obtained in some studies.

42   For hereditary disease the adoption of a DDREF of 3 is supported by experimental data in mice.

REFERENCES

1   ICRP. Recommendations of the International Commission on Radiological Protection. ICRP Publication 60. *Ann ICRP*, **21**, Nos 1–3 (1991).

2   National Council on Radiation Protection and Measurements. Influence of dose and its distribution in time on dose–response relationships for low-LET radiation. Washington DC, NCRP, Report No. 64 (1980).

3   Pierce, D A, and Vaeth, M. The shape of the cancer mortality dose-response curve for atomic bomb survivors. Hiroshima, Radiation Effects Research Foundation, Report TR7-89 (1989).

4   Pierce, D A, and Vaeth, M. Cancer risk estimation from the A-bomb survivors: Extrapolation to low doses, use of relative risk models and other uncertainties. IN *Low Dose Radiation: Biological Bases of Risk Assessment* (Eds K F Baverstock and J W Stather). London, Taylor and Francis (1989).

5   ICRP. Recommendations of the International Commission on Radiological Protection. ICRP Publication 26. *Ann. ICRP*, **1**, No. 3 (1977).

6   Stather, J W, Muirhead, C R, Edwards, A A, Harrison. J D, Lloyd, D C, and Wood, N R. Health effects models developed from the 1988 UNSCEAR report. Chilton, NRPB-R226 (1988) (London, HMSO).

7   UNSCEAR. Sources and effects of ionizing radiation. 1977 report to the General Assembly, with annexes. New York, United Nations (1977).

8   UNSCEAR. Genetic and somatic effects of ionizing radiation. 1986 Report to the General Assembly, with annexes. New York, United Nations (1986).

9   UNSCEAR. Sources, effects and risks of ionizing radiation. 1988 Report to the General Assembly, with annexes. New York, United Nations (1988).

10   Abrahamson, S, Bender, M, Book, C, *et al*. Health effects models for nuclear power plant accident consequence analysis. Low LET radiation, Part II: Scientific bases for health effects models. Washington DC, US Nuclear Regulatory Commission, NUREG/CR- 4214, SANDS85-7185 Rev.1, Part II (1989).

11   Abrahamson, S, Bender, M A, Boecker, B B, *et al*. Health effects models for nuclear power plant accident consequence analysis. Modifications of models resulting from recent reports on health effects of ionizing radiation. Low-LET radiation. Part II: Scientific bases for health effects models. Washington DC, US Nuclear Regulatory Commission, NUREG/CR-4214, Revision 1, Add. 1 LMF-132 (1991).

12   Thacker, J, Wilson, R E, and Goodhead, D T. The induction of chromosome aberrations by carbon ultrasoft x rays in V79 hamster cells. *Int. J. Radiat. Biol.,* **49**, 645–56 (1986).

13   BEIR IV. Health risks of radon and other internally deposited alpha-emitters. Washington DC, NAS/NRC (1988).

14   BEIR V. Health effects of exposure to low levels of ionizing radiation. Washington DC, NAS/NRC (1990).

15   Sacher, G A, and Grahn, D. Survival of mice under duration of life exposure to gamma rays. I The dosage-survival relationship and the lethality fraction. *J. Natl Cancer Inst.,* **32**, 277 (1964).

16   Thomson, J F, and Grahn, D. Life shortening in mice exposed to fission neutrons and γ-rays. *Radiat. Res.,* **118**, 151–60 (1989).

17   Thomson, J F, Williamson, F S, Grahn, D, *et al*. Life shortening in mice exposed to fission neutrons and γ-rays. II. Single and short term fractionated exposures. *Radiat. Res.,* **86**, 559–72 (1981).

18   Thomson, J F, and Grahn, D. Life shortening in mice exposed to fission neutrons and γ-rays. VII Effects of 60 once-weekly exposures. *Radiat. Res.,* **115**, 347–60 (1988).

19   Mole, R H, and Major, I R. Myeloid leukaemia frequency after protracted exposure to ionizing radiation: Experimental confirmation of the flat dose-response found in ankylosing spondylitis after a single treatment course with X rays. *Leuk. Res.,* **7**, 295 (1983).

20   Upton, A C, Randoloh, M L, and Conklin, J W. Late effects of fast neutrons and gamma-rays in mice as influenced by the dose rate of irradiation: Induction of neoplasia. *Radiat. Res.,* **41**, 467–91 (1970).

21   Ullrich, R L, and Storer, J B. Influence of γ irradiation on the development of neoplastic disease in mice. III. Dose-rate effects. *Radiat. Res.,* **80**, 325–42 (1979).

22   Ullrich, R L, and Storer, J B. Influence of dose, dose rate and radiation quality on radiation carcinogenesis and life shortening in RFM and BALB/c mice. IN *Late Effects of Ionizing Radiation*. Vienna, IAEA, Volume 2, p 95 (1978).

23   Griffith, W C, Boecker, B B, Cuddihy, R G, *et al*. Preliminary radiation risk estimates of carcinoma incidence in the lung as a function of cumulative radiation dose using proportional tumour incidence rates. Albuquerque, LMF-120/UC-48 (1987).

24   Gragtmans, N J, Myers, D K, Johnson, J R, *et al*. Occurrence of mammary tumours in rats after exposure to tritium β rays and 200-kVp x rays. *Radiat. Res.,* **99**, 636–50 (1984).

25   Shellabarger, C J, and Brown, R D. Rat mammary neoplasia following cobalt 60 irradiation at 0.3R or 10R per minute. *Radiat. Res.,* **51**, 493–4 (1972).

26   Broerse, J J, Hennen, L A, van Zwicken, M J, *et al*. Dose-effect relations for mammary carcinogenesis in different rat strains after irradiation with x-rays and monoenergetic neutrons. IN *Biological Effects of Low-Level Radiation With Special Regard to Stochastic and Non-stochastic Effects*. Vienna, IAEA, pp 507–20 (1983).

27   Ullrich, R L, and Storer, J B. Influence of γ irradiation on the development of neoplastic disease in mice. II. Solid tumours. *Radiat. Res.,* **80**, 317–24 (1979).

28   Walinder, G. Late effects of irradiation on the thyroid gland in mice. I. Irradiation of adult mice. *Acta Radiol. Ther. Phys. Biol.,* **2**, 433–51 (1972).

29   Doniach, I. Effects including carcinogenesis of iodine-131 and X-rays on the thyroid of experimental animals: A review. *Health Phys.,* **9,** 1357–62 (1963).

30   Lee, W, Chiacchierini, R P, and Shleien, B, *et al*. Thyroid tumours following I-131 or localized x-irradiation to the thyroid and pituitary glands in rats. *Radiat. Res.,* **92,** 307–19 (1982).

31   Ullrich, R L, Jernigan, M C, Satterfield, L C, *et al*. Radiation-carcinogenesis: Time-dose relationships. *Radiat. Res.,* **111,** 179–84 (1987).

32   Thomson, J F, Williamson, F S, and Grahn, D. Life shortening in mice exposed to fission neutrons and x-rays III. Neutron exposures of 5 and 10 rad. *Radiat. Res.,* **93,** 205–9 (1983).

33   Carnes, B A, Grahn, D, and Thomson J F. Dose-response modelling of life shortening in a retrospective analysis of the combined data for the JANUS programme at Argonne National Laboratory. *Radiat. Res.,* **119,** 39–56 (1989).

34   Storer, J B, Serrano, L J, Darden, E B, *et al*. Life shortening in RFM and BALB/c mice as a function of radiation quality, dose and dose rate. *Radiat. Res.,* **78,** 122–61 (1979).

35   Storer, J B, and Ullrich, R L. Life shortening in BALB/c mice following brief, protracted or fractionated exposures to neutrons. *Radiat. Res.,* **96,** 335–47 (1983).

36   Maisin, J R, Wambersie, A, Gerber, G B, *et al*. Life-shortening and disease incidence in C57B1 mice after single and fractionated γ and high-energy neutron exposure. *Radiat. Res.,* **113,** 300–317 (1988).

37   Grahn, D, and Carnes, B A. Quoted in Fry, 1990 (reference 38).

38   Fry, R J M. Time-dose relationship and high LET irradiation. *Int. J. Radiat. Biol.,* **58,** 866–70 (1990).

39   Ullrich, R L. Tumour induction in BALB/c mice after fractionated or protracted exposures to fission spectrum neutrons. *Radiat. Res.,* **97,** 587–97 (1984).

40   Vogel, H H, and Dickson, N W. Mammary neoplasia in Sprague-Dawley rats following acute and protracted irradiation. IN *Proceedings European Seminar on Neutron Carcinogenesis* (Eds J J Broerse and G B Gerber). Luxembourg, CEC (1982).

41   Fry, R J M. The role of animal species in low dose extrapolation. IN: *Proceedings 10th Annual Meeting of the National Council on Radiation Protection and Measurement. Critical issues in setting dose limits.* Washington DC, NCRP, pp 109–18 (1982).

42   Huiskamp, R, Davids, J A G, and Mole, R H. Acute myeloid leukaemia induction in CBA/H mice by irradiation with fission neutrons as a function of exposure rate. IN: *Radiation Research. A Twentieth-Century Perspective* (Eds J D Chapman, W C Dewey and G F Whitmore). London, Academic Press, Volume 1, p 258 (1991).

43   Stather, J W. Effects of α-particle irradiation on carcinogenesis. *Int. J. Radiat. Biol.,* **58,** 871–4 (1990).

44   Goldman, M. Experimental carcinogenesis in the skeleton. IN: *Radiation Carcinogenesis* (Eds A C Upton, R E Albert, F J Burns and R E Shore) London, Elsevier, pp 214–31 (1986).

45   Thompson, R C. Life-span effects of ionizing radiation in the beagle dog. Washington DC, PNL-6822 UC-408, US DOE (1989).

46   Sanders, C L, and Mahaffey, J A. Inhalation carcinogenesis of high-fired $^{244}CmO_2$ in rats. *Radiat. Res.,* **76,** 384–401 (1978).

47   Lundgren, D L, Gillett, A, and Hahn, F F. Effects of protraction of the α dose to the lungs of mice by repeated inhalation exposure to aerosols of $^{239}PuO_2$. *Radiat. Res.,* **111,** 201–24 (1987).

48   Little, J B, Kennedy, A R, and McGandy, R B. Effect of dose rate on the induction of experimental lung cancer in hamsters by α radiation. *Health Phys.,* **103,** 293–9 (1985).

49   Cross, F. A review of experimental animal radon health effects data. IN: *Radiation Research. A Twentieth-Century Perspective* (Eds W C Dewey, M Edington, R J M Fry, E S Hall and G F Whitmore). San Diego, Academic Press, Volume 2, pp 476–81 (1991).

50   Balcer-Kubiczek, E K, and Harrison, G H. Survival and oncogenic transformation of C3H/10T1/2 cells after extended x irradiation. *Radiat. Res.,* **104,** 214–23 (1985).

51   Balcer-Kubiczek, E K, Harrison, G H, and Thompson, B W. Repair time for oncogenic transformation in C3H/10T1/2 cells subjected to protracted x irradiation. *Int. J. Radiat. Biol.,* **51,** 219–26 (1987).

52   Han, A, Hill, C K, and Elkind, M M. Repair processes and radiation quality in neoplastic transformation of mammalian cells. *Radiat. Res.,* **99,** 249–61 (1984).

53   Hill, C K, Carnes, B A, Han, A, *et al*. Neoplastic transformation is enhanced by multiple low doses of fission spectrum neutrons. *Radiat. Res.,* **102,** 404–10 (1985).

54   Miller, R C, Geard, C R, Brenner, D J, *et al.* The effects of temporal distribution of dose on neutron-induced transformation. IN: *Cell Transformation and Radiation-Induced Cancer* (Eds K H Chadwick, C Seymour and B Barnhart). Bristol, Adam Hilger, pp 357–62 (1989).

55   Rossi, H H, and Kellerer, A M. The dose rate dependence of oncogenic transformations by neutrons may be due to variation of response during the cell cycle. *Int. J. Radiat. Biol.*, **50**, 353–61 (1986).

56   Brenner, D J, and Hall, E H. The inverse dose-rate effect for oncogenic transformation by neutrons and charged particles: A plausible interpretation consistent with published data. *Int. J. Radiat. Biol.*, **58**, 748–58 (1990).

57   Hall, E J. Finding a smoother pebble: A workshop summary. IN: *Cell Transformation and Radiation-induced Cancer* (Eds K H Chadwick, C Seymour and B Barnhart). Bristol, Adam Hilger, pp 401–12 (1989).

58   Thacker, J. The measurement of radiation-induced mutation in mammalian cells at low doses and dose rates. *Adv. Radiat. Biol.*, **16**, 77–124 (1992).

59   Hahn, G M, and Little, J B. Plateau-phase culture of mammalian cells in an *in vitro* model for human cancer. *Can. Topics Radiat. Res. Quost.*, **8**, 39–83 (1972).

60   Mitchell, J B, Bedford, J S, and Bailey, S K. Dose rate effects in mammalian cells in culture. III. Comparison of cell killing and cell proliferation during continuous irradiation for six different cell lines. *Radiat. Res.*, **79**, 537–51 (1979).

61   Thacker, J, and Stretch, A. Recovery from lethal and mutagenic damage during post-irradiation holding and low-dose-rate irradiation of cultured hamster cells. *Radiat. Res.*, **96**, 380–92 (1983).

62   Iliakis, G. The influence of conditions affecting repair and fixation of potentially lethal damage on the induction of 6-thioguanine resistance after exposure of mammalian cells to x-rays. *Mutat. Res.*, **126**, 215–25 (1984).

63   Furuno-Fukushi, I, Ueno, A M, and Matsudaira, H. Mutation induction by very low dose rate gamma-rays in cultured mouse leukaemia cells L5178Y. *Radiat. Res.* **15**, 273–80 (1988).

64   Furuno-Fukushi, I, Aoki, A, and Matsudaira, H. Mutation induction by different dose rates of γ rays in near-diploid mouse cells in plateau and log phase culture. *Radiation Research* (In press).

65   Shimizu, Y, Kato, H, Schull, W J, *et al.* Life Span Study Report II, Part I: Comparison of risk coefficients for site-specific cancer mortality based on the DS86 and T65DR shielded kerma and organ doses. Hiroshima, Radiation Effects Research Foundation, Report TR12–87 (1987).

66   Shimizu, Y, Kato, H, and Schull, W J. Life Span Study Report II, Part II: Cancer mortality in the years 1950–1985 based on the recently revised doses (DS86). Hiroshima, Radiation Effects Research Foundation, Report TR5–88 (1988).

67   Shore, R E, Woodard, E, Hildreth, N, *et al.* Thyroid tumours following thymus irradiation. *J. Natl Cancer Inst.*, **74**, 1177–84 (1985).

68   Ron, E, and Modan, B. Thyroid and other neoplasms following childhood scalp irradiation. IN: *Radiation Carcinogenesis – Epidemiology and Biological Significance* (Eds J D Boice, Jr, and J F Franmeni, Jr). New York, Raven Press, pp 139–52 (1984).

69   Bithell, J F, and Stewart, A M. Pre-natal irradiation and childhood malignancy: A review of British data from the Oxford Survey. *Br. J. Cancer*, **31**, 271–87 (1975).

70   Muirhead, C R, and Kneale, G W. Pre-natal irradiation and childhood cancer. *J. Radiol. Prot.*, **9**, 209–12 (1989).

71   Holm, L E, Lundell, G, and Walinder, G. Incidence of malignant thyroid tumours in humans after exposure to diagnostic doses of iodine-131: I. Retrospective cohort study. *J. Natl Cancer Inst.*, **64**, 1055–9 (1980).

72   Holm, L E, Wiklund, K E, Lundell, G E, *et al.* Thyroid cancer after diagnostic doses of iodine-131: A retrospective cohort study. *J. Natl Cancer Inst.*, **80**, 1132–8 (1988).

73   Holm, L E, Wiklund, K E, Lundell, G E, *et al*. Cancer risk in population examined with diagnostic doses of ^{131}I. *J. Natl Cancer Inst.*, **81**, 302–6 (1989).

74   Miller, A B, Howe, G R, Sherman, G J, *et al.* Mortality from breast cancer after irradiation during fluoroscopic examinations in patients being treated for tuberculosis. *N. Engl. J. Med.*, **321**, 1285–9 (1989).

75   Kendall, G M, Muirhead, C R, MacGibbon, B H, O'Hagan, J A, Conquest, A J, Goodill, A A, Butland, B K, Fell, T P, Jackson, D A, Webb, M A, Haylock, R G E, Thomas, J M and Silk, T J. Mortality and occupational exposure to radiation: First analysis of the National Registry for Radiation Workers. *Br. Med. J.*, **304**, 220–5 (1992).

76   Searle, A G. Mutation induction in mice. *Adv. Radiat. Biol.*, **4**, 131–207 (1974).

77 Russell, W L, and Kelly, E M. Mutation frequencies in male mice and the estimation of genetic hazards of radiation in man. *Proc. Natl Acad. Sci., USA,* **79,** 542–4 (1982).

78 Russell, W L, Russell, L B, and Kelly, E M. Radiation dose rate and mutation frequency. *Science,* **128,** 1546–50 (1958).

79 Russell, W L. The effect of radiation dose and fractionation on mutation rate in mice. IN: *Repair from Genetic Radiation Damage* (Ed F J Sobels). Oxford, Pergamon Press (1963).

80 Lyon, M F, Phillips, R J S, and Bailey, H J. Mutagenic effect of repeated small radiation doses to mouse spermatogonia. I Specific locus mutation rates. *Mutat. Res.,* **15,** 185–90 (1972).

81 Selby, P B, Lee, S S, Kelly, E M, *et al.* Specific-locus experiments show that female mice exposed near the time of birth to low-LET radiation exhibit both a low mutational response and a dose-rate effect. Submitted to *Mutation Research* (1991).

82 UNSCEAR. Ionizing radiation: Levels and effects. Report to the General Assembly, with annexes. New York, United Nations (1972).

4 Radiation-induced Cancer

EPIDEMIOLOGICAL STUDIES

1   Information on the risks of cancer following radiation exposure has been obtained from a variety of studies of human populations. These studies have been reviewed by UNSCEAR[1] and BEIR[2,3]. The studies generally fall into three classes: the study of the survivors of the atomic bombings of Hiroshima and Nagasaki in Japan in 1945, studies of populations exposed for medical reasons, and studies of groups exposed occupationally. In order to examine the usefulness of these studies for risk assessment, the following features can be used to distinguish the studies (see Table 4.1).

Population size and length of follow-up

2   The statistical power to detect and to estimate the radiation-induced cancer risk increases with both the size of the irradiated population under study and the length of time over which this population is followed. In this regard, the study of the Japanese atomic bomb survivors is very well placed. In some cases it may be possible to increase statistical power by combining results from different studies. However, care needs to be taken to ensure that the data being combined are similar in other respects (as described below).

Range of ages of exposure, sexes and ethnic groups

3   The range of ages of exposure and sexes in certain groups with medical exposures may be restricted by virtue of the form of the original disease. For example, ankylosing spondylitis arises mainly amongst young adult males, ringworm of the scalp was treated mainly in childhood, and some cancers are sex specific. Similarly, occupational studies do not include children. Consequently, such studies on their own cannot be used to derive risk estimates associated with exposure at all ages and for both sexes. The study of the Japanese atomic bomb survivors, in contrast, has the advantage that it allows risks associated with exposure of the general population to be calculated. However, a disadvantage in calculating risks for a western population is that this study is specific to a Japanese population, unlike some of the other studies in Table 4.1. The topic of transferring radiation-induced cancer risks across populations with different baseline rates is discussed later in this chapter.

Reason for receiving exposure

4   Medically irradiated populations differ from the others considered here in that they received exposure because of illness. Studies of such populations usually examine and take into account whether the original illness may have affected the subsequent risk of cancer. However, even when this is not the case, there is the question of whether, because of their illness, medically irradiated groups are different from the general population. One way of addressing this question is to check whether risk estimates obtained from these studies are consistent with those from other types of study.

Whether or not irradiation is whole body

5   In many of the medically irradiated populations, the exposure is partial body. Consequently such studies cannot, by themselves, be used to derive risks associated with exposure of the whole body, unlike the study of the Japanese atomic bomb

TABLE 4.1 *Features of some epidemiological studies of radiation-induced cancer risks*

	Life Span Study (LSS) Japanese atomic bomb survivors (Shimizu et al[4])	Ankylosing Spondylitis Study (ASS) (Darby et al[5])	Canadian tuberculosis patients given chest fluoroscopies (Miller et al[6])	Children in Israel irradiated for ringworm of the scalp (Ron et al[7-9])	UK National Registry for Radiation Workers (Kendall et al[10])
Population size	75 991 (with DS86 doses)	14 106	31 701	10 834	95 217
Period of follow-up	5–40 years following exposure	Up to 38 years (mean 13 years)*	Up to 30 years (mean 27 years)	Up to 32 years (mean 26 years)	Up to 34 years (mean 12.7 years)
Ranges of:					
(i) ages at exposure	All	Virtually all ≥ 15 years	At least 10 years	0–15 years	18–64 years
(ii) sexes	Similar numbers of males and females	83% male	Female	Similar numbers of males and females	92% male
(iii) ethnic groups	Japanese	Western (UK)	Western (North American)	African, Asian	Western (UK)
Setting in which exposure was received	War	Medical: therapy for non-malignant disease	Medical: diagnostic	Medical: therapy for non-malignant disease	Occupational
Range of organs irradiated	All	All (but mainly those in proximity to spine)	Mainly breast and lung	Mainly brain, bone marrow, thyroid, skin, breast	All
Availability of dose estimates	Organ doses – individual basis	Mean organ doses – individually only for red bone marrow at present	Organ doses – individual basis	Brain, thyroid and skin doses – individual basis	Individual whole-body external doses
Range of doses	Mainly 0–4 Gy	Mainly 0–20 Gy	Mainly 0–10 Gy	Brain: 0–6 Gy (mean 1.5 Gy) Thyroid: 0–0.5 Gy (mean 0.09 Gy)	Mainly 0–0.5 Sv (mean 0.034 Sv)
Dose rate	High	High	High, but highly fractionated	High	Low
Radiation quality	Mainly low LET	Low LET	Low LET	Low LET	Mainly low LET

* About half the patients in the ASS received more than one course of X-rays, and were removed from the study at the time of the second course (mean follow-up 3.5 years). The remaining half, who received only one course of X-rays, had a mean follow-up of 23.6 years.

survivors for example. However, the medical studies may contain more information on the risks for specific, heavily irradiated organs (such as bone, skin, thyroid and liver) than do the studies of whole-body exposure.

Availability of organ dose estimates on an individual basis

6   In order to derive estimates of risk per unit dose for particular cancer sites, the doses to specific organs are required. Studies of medically exposed groups should be well placed in this respect, since it is often possible to estimate organ doses on the basis of records of the relevant medical procedure. However, large heterogeneity in the exposure of different organs may give rise to substantial uncertainty in the corresponding dose estimates. Furthermore, doses should, if possible, be obtained on an individual basis if it is thought that exposures are likely to vary considerably between subjects in a study. In the study of the Japanese atomic bomb survivors, for example, doses were calculated on the basis of the individuals' positions at the time of the bombing and the shielding provided by building, terrain, etc[11].

Range of doses

7   Some medically exposed groups, such as patients given radiotherapy for a first cancer who are later followed to see if they have developed a second cancer, may receive very high local doses while organs away from the treated site may receive considerably smaller doses. Consequently, to make estimates of risks at low doses from such studies requires information on the shape of the dose–response relationship based, for example, on radiobiological considerations. Studies of populations exposed at low doses, whilst directly relevant to the needs of radiation protection, can be very difficult to interpret, owing to the generally low statistical power to detect any excess risk at low doses and the potential for confounding factors to either exaggerate or hide any risk. Studies of people exposed over a wide range of doses, however, allow risks at low doses to be assessed by both direct observation on those exposed at such doses and the extrapolation of risks observed at high doses. In studies of this type, such as those of the Japanese atomic bomb survivors and of women with multiple chest fluoroscopies, indications can be obtained as to which forms of the dose–response relationship are consistent with the data, although generally the data are not strong enough to allow a precise formulation of this relationship to be derived (see paragraphs 47–50).

Dose rate

8   Most studies in radiation epidemiology are of populations exposed at high dose rates, although for medically exposed groups, such as women with multiple chest fluoroscopies, the doses were highly fractionated. Using these studies to predict risks associated with low dose rate exposures therefore requires additional information, based for example on radiobiological considerations. Studies of those with low dose rate exposures received occupationally or from natural radiation are directly relevant for radiological protection purposes. However, as pointed out above, these studies may be affected by lack of statistical power and/or confounding factors. This topic is further discussed in paragraph 51 and in Appendix B.

Radiation quality

9   The Japanese atomic bomb survivors and many of the groups irradiated for medical reasons were exposed, either predominantly or entirely, to low LET radiation.

However, for other groups such as patients given radium-224 for ankylosing spondylitis[12], patients given Thorotrast (an X-ray contrast medium)[2], luminous dial painters with intakes of radium-226 and radon-exposed miners[2], the exposures were to high LET radiation. There are some difficulties in using data from studies of high LET exposures to estimate the risks associated with low LET exposures since, as pointed out in Chapter 7, the ratio of the risks associated with the two types of exposure varies with dose and dose rate. Therefore, as far as possible, the evaluation of risks associated with low LET exposure will be based on studies with such exposure. Similarly, risks associated with high LET exposures from radon will be based on studies of radon exposed groups.

Conclusions on studies to be used for risk estimation

10 On the basis of the above considerations, the follow-up of the Japanese atomic bomb survivors is the best single source of data for use in estimating the risk of cancer in a population of all ages and both sexes, exposed to low LET radiation. While the medical studies do provide a considerable amount of information about the risks for certain organs, it is difficult to bring together this information in the same way as for the Japanese data. Therefore the risk estimates presented here for exposure of a UK population to low LET radiation will be based primarily on the Japanese data, but with supporting and additional evidence supplied by other studies. This is similar to the approach of the BEIR V Committee in calculating risk estimates for the population of the USA[3] and that used previously for a UK population[13].

11 Issues affecting the calculation of cancer risk estimates are discussed in paragraphs 12–56 and the estimates themselves are presented in paragraphs 57–77. In paragraphs 78–97 the risks associated with radon and its progeny are examined, based primarily on studies of occupationally exposed miners[2]. The emphasis here is on cancer since epidemiological studies have generally not shown an excess of non-cancer mortality. A recent report[14] based on the follow-up of the Japanese atomic bomb survivors to 1985 has, in contrast, provided some evidence of an excess of non-cancer mortality for doses in excess of 2 Gy. Whilst the interpretation of this result is problematical, the absence of any trend with doses less than 1–2 Gy suggests that non-cancer mortality is unlikely to be relevant for doses encountered in the context of radiological protection.

CALCULATION OF RISK ESTIMATES

Empirical and mechanistic models

12 In analysing data on radiation-induced cancers among populations exposed to high doses, empirically based models have generally been used to describe the variation in risks with time since exposure and across populations. In particular, the simple relative (multiplicative) and absolute (additive) risk models have commonly been used for solid cancers, eg by UNSCEAR[1] and ICRP[15]. Under these models the excess relative risk or the annual absolute excess risk, respectively, is assumed to be constant over time and/or populations, over the period of 10 or more years following exposure in the case of most solid cancers. For both models the risk coefficients may vary additionally by sex and age at exposure. Since the baseline rates for solid cancers increase rapidly with age, the assumption of constant relative risks over time yields a higher estimate of lifetime risk

than does the corresponding absolute risk model. More general models have also been utilised, such as a hybrid model that reduces to either the simple relative or absolute risk model as special cases. Furthermore, models under which the relative risk varies with time since exposure were developed in the report of the BEIR V Committee[3].

13   An alternative approach involves modelling the underlying carcinogenic process. As noted in Chapter 2, there is clear evidence for the multistage nature of tumour induction, and mathematical models that seek to describe this process have been developed. One particular example is the multistage model of Armitage and Doll[16], under which it is assumed that a cell becomes malignant as a result of a number of irreversible heritable changes. This model predicts that cancer incidence rates vary as a power function of age, which appears to be true for many solid cancers. If a carcinogen acts at the jth out of k stages in the above process, then it has been shown[17] that the relative risk (RR) following a single exposure to this carcinogen is

$$RR = 1 + \eta b^{j-1} t^{k-j-1}/a^{k-1}, \qquad (4.1)$$

where b denotes age at exposure, t denotes time since exposure, a denotes attained age, and η varies according to the level of exposure. If the carcinogen acts at an early stage, then the relative risk tends not to vary too much with time since exposure (except soon after exposure for those exposed when young) but decreases with increasing age at exposure. If the carcinogen acts at a later stage under the multistage model, then the absolute risk is fairly constant with time since exposure but increases with increasing age at exposure. There are thus parallels with the simple relative and absolute risk models referred to earlier for the projection of risks over time. Predictions of the joint effect of two carcinogens can also be made[17] under the Armitage–Doll model; this may be relevant in examining how radiation-induced risks vary across populations with differing baseline cancer rates.

14   Armitage–Doll multistage models and other mechanistic models, such as that of Moolgavkar and Knudson[18] have been used to study carcinogens such as cigarette smoke[19] and asbestos[20], as well as radiation[21–23]. Furthermore, study of cellular and molecular mechanisms now provides unambiguous evidence for the multistage nature of tumour induction (see Chapter 2). However, mathematical mechanistic models have sometimes been criticised for not being sufficiently realistic (eg Pearce[20]). In practice, only two or three stages have been identified experimentally[3].

15   In the absence of detailed information on the processes underlying tumour initiation, promotion and progression, priority is given here to risk projections based on empirically derived models. However, by way of comparison, some results will be given based on fitting Armitage–Doll multistage models to epidemiological data on radiation-induced cancer. This is not to suggest that these models provide an accurate description of carcinogenesis; rather the aim is to illustrate the application of mechanistic models which, as they are refined, may well be of increasing importance in the future.

Projection of risks over time

16   Very few epidemiological studies have followed the entire study population until the end of life. For example, at the time of the last published follow-up, to 1985[4], the Japanese atomic bomb survivors had been followed up to 40 years after exposure, and about two-thirds of this population were still alive. Those who were exposed when

young are only now reaching the ages when solid cancers would normally be more likely to occur. Consequently some means is required of projecting risks beyond the period of follow-up in order to estimate the cancer risk over a whole lifetime.

17   For leukaemia, the temporal pattern of risk observed in studies such as the Life Span Study (LSS) of Japanese atomic bomb survivors[4] and the Ankylosing Spondylitis Study (ASS) of UK patients treated with radiation[5] is of a peak within about 4–7 years of exposure followed by a tailing-off in risk. However, the analysis by the BEIR V Committee[3] of the LSS data did indicate a slower decrease over time for those irradiated as adults than for those irradiated as children. Under the model derived by BEIR from these data, the relative risk for those aged 20 years or less at exposure is higher during the period 2–15 years following exposure than thereafter; whereas for those aged more than 20 years at exposure the relative risk is higher up to 25 years following exposure than thereafter. Based on this model, most of the risk is predicted to be expressed within the current period of follow-up for the LSS, ie up to 40 years post-exposure, although a few radiation-induced leukaemias may occur beyond this time.

18   For bone cancer, analysis of data on patients given radium-224 suggests a similar temporal pattern of risk to that for leukaemia[12].

19   For the grouping of all cancers other than leukaemia, Shimizu *et al*[4] showed that excess deaths in the LSS in the most recent follow-up to 1985 appeared to increase over time in direct proportion to the increase in natural cancer mortality with age. After adjustment for age at exposure, the relative risks appeared to be approximately constant over time. A possible exception to this finding concerns those aged less than 10 years at time of exposure, for whom there is a suggestion of a fall in the relative risk. A later analysis[24] of the LSS and some groups with medical exposures also suggested a decrease in the relative risk with time since exposure for those irradiated in childhood. This is especially important since the relative risks increase with decreasing age at exposure, and so the youngest age cohorts would show the highest lifetime risk if the relative risk were to remain constant until the end of life. However, since those in the LSS irradiated at less than 10 years are only now attaining the ages at which solid tumours would normally occur, the absolute excess risk averaged over the follow-up to date is lower than in older age cohorts. After adjusting for attained age, the absolute risk appears to be higher for the younger cohort. Consequently there is substantial uncertainty in the eventual lifetime risk for the youngest age cohort.

20   The study of the incidence of second cancers in women treated with radiation for cervical cancer[25] also suggested that the relative risk for solid tumours is approximately constant up to at least 30 years following exposure. However, analyses based on the follow-up to 1982 of the ASS[5,26] revealed a tailing-off in the radiation-induced risk for the groupings of all cancer except leukaemia and colon cancer, both on relative and absolute scales, from about 20 years following exposure. This discrepancy might, in part, be explained by differences in temporal patterns of risk for different cancer types. Whilst the data for individual cancer types are sometimes not sufficiently strong to allow these patterns to be distinguished, those data that are available are reviewed here.

Lung cancer

21   The BEIR IV Committee[2] performed a joint analysis of data from four groups of miners exposed to radon. The model so derived was such that the relative risk decreased after 15 years following exposure, but remained constant thereafter. The

BEIR V model for respiratory cancer also allowed for a tailing-off in the relative risk, in this case varying as an inverse power of time since exposure[3]. Although this effect had not been statistically significant in the LSS, to which the BEIR V model was fitted, the trend with time since exposure was included in the model on the basis of the pattern seen in the ASS[5]. A factor that may bear upon these temporal trends is the effect of smoking (see paragraphs 34 and 35).

Breast cancer

22   Studies of breast cancer incidence among the Japanese atomic bomb survivors[27], women in New York State treated for acute postpartum mastitis with X-rays[28] and tuberculosis patients in Massachusetts given multiple chest fluoroscopies[29] suggest constancy of the relative risk (adjusted for age at exposure) up to at least 40 years following exposure. However, among Canadian tuberculosis patients[6], the relative risk of breast cancer mortality appeared to decrease after 35 years following fluoroscopic examinations. The BEIR V combined analysis of these data sets produced models for incidence and mortality under which the relative risk peaks at 15–20 years after exposure and then decreases. However, it has now been realised that the Japanese incidence data used in the BEIR V analysis were incorrect, and that the evidence for a decline in the relative risk may not be as strong as indicated in that analysis. A new parallel analysis of the data sets on breast cancer incidence is currently being performed[30]. Whilst the Japanese mortality data were not in error, the BEIR V model for breast cancer mortality may be invalid owing to the decision made – largely on the basis of the incidence data – to assume constancy of the underlying relative risk across populations (see also paragraphs 31 and 32). Since the mortality data from Japan yield an excess relative risk about two to three times that from the Canadian study[3], the temporal pattern in the BEIR V model for mortality may be an artefact due to combining data sets with different lengths of follow-up. The new analysis of the incidence data should be informative in indicating whether there really is an indication of a decrease in the relative risk over time.

Digestive cancers

23   The BEIR V Committee analysed this set of cancers as a group. Based on analysis of the LSS data, a model under which the relative risk remains constant with time since exposure was recommended[3]. With detailed data files for the LSS supplied by the Radiation Effects Research Foundation (RERF) in Japan, further analyses have been undertaken at the Board which indicate that the relative risks for two of the main types of digestive cancer, namely stomach cancer and colon cancer, also appear to remain constant over the period of follow-up (see Appendix A).

Other cancers

24   All cancers other than leukaemia, respiratory, breast and digestive cancers were analysed as a group by the BEIR V Committee using the LSS data. The model so produced was of the form of a constant relative risk over time[3]. Although, based on the LSS, the data for individual cancer types within the above grouping may not be strong enough to allow the temporal pattern of risk to be discerned clearly, other data sets do provide information for the following types of cancer.

25   *Thyroid cancer* Among patients in New York State treated with X-rays for enlarged thymus in childhood[31], the pattern of thyroid cancer incidence with time since

exposure seemed to be consistent with constancy of the absolute risk rather than the relative risk, although there was an indication of a decrease in the absolute risk beyond 25 years following exposure. However, a study of thyroid cancer incidence among children in Israel irradiated for *tinea capitis* (ringworm of the scalp) indicated constancy of the relative risk over time[8]. The reason for the different patterns seen in the two studies is not clear.

26   *Skin cancer*   Studies of two groups of children irradiated for ringworm of the scalp are consistent with the relative risks of skin cancer incidence being constant over time. However, both in the study in Israel[9] and in that in New York[24,32], there was an indication that the relative risk may decrease after 25 years following exposure.

Conclusions on temporal pattern

27   The data for solid cancers are more consistent with constancy of relative rather than absolute risks over time[3]. Consequently, although models under which the absolute risk varies with time since exposure may be fitted to these data, it is simpler to consider models for relative risks in general. However, there are still uncertainties about whether relative risks remain constant or decrease at long times after exposure. There are also suggestions of different temporal patterns for different cancer types; for example, there seems to be more evidence of a decrease in relative risks for lung cancer than for digestive cancers. In view of the above uncertainties, risk estimates for most solid cancers will be presented for two types of empirical model: one based on the assumption of the constancy of relative risks throughout a lifetime and the other based on the risk up to 40 years following exposure (the period covered by the latest follow-up of the LSS). For lung cancer, the BEIR V time varying relative risk model will be considered. As stated above (paragraphs 12–15), estimates based on fitting Armitage–Doll multistage models to the LSS data will also be presented by way of comparison. Since these models predict that the relative risks vary over time (to a small or a large extent depending on the stage at which radiation is modelled as acting), the risks estimated under these models will generally lie between the values based on the risk up to 40 years and the lifetime relative risk projection, respectively. It should, however, be emphasised that the application of multistage models is intended only to illustrate the use of mechanistic models, rather than to suggest that these models provide an accurate description of carcinogenesis.

Transfer of risks across populations

28   For some types of cancer, baseline cancer rates vary widely between countries. For example, rates for stomach, lung and breast cancer vary – in differing directions – from two-fold to six-fold between Japan and western countries such as the UK[33]. These differences reflect the effects of genetic factors and factors related to ethnic origin, or environmental factors such as smoking, hormonal status and diet[19]. In order to use data from, for example, the Japanese atomic bomb survivors to estimate risks for specific cancers in a UK population, the method of transferring risks across populations is therefore of importance. However, it should be pointed out that the *total* cancer risk is less sensitive to the method of transferring risks[34]. The method of transferring risks depends on judgements concerning the interaction between radiation and factors that influence the baseline cancer risk. In the absence of a clear understanding of the relevant biological mechanisms, the approaches that have generally been taken involve

assuming constancy of either relative or absolute risks across populations. These two empirical models are equivalent to assuming that the joint effect of radiation and other factors on the cancer risk is multiplicative or additive, respectively.

29 Some results from applying these models are shown in Table 4.2. Estimates of risks in a UK population based on the LSS data from Japan are given for:

(i) a model under which the relative risk is constant both across populations and over time,

(ii) a model under which the *absolute* risk is constant across populations but the *relative* risk is constant over time (referred to by Land and Sinclair[34] as the 'NIH' model).

Under the former model the highest risks arise for organs such as lung that have the highest rates in the UK. Under the latter (NIH) model, however, the highest risks are for organs such as stomach that have the highest rates in Japan. As a consequence the estimates of risk for some organs differ substantially between the two models. For stomach cancer the risk based on an additive transfer across populations is about 6 times that based on a multiplicative transfer, whereas the risks for lung cancer and breast cancer under the latter model are, respectively, 1.8 and 4.6 times the corresponding values under the former model. However, for the grouping of all cancers, the risks differ only by about 30%.

Cancer type	Deaths (10^{-2} Sv^{-1})	
	Model	
	Multiplicative	NIH
All except leukaemia	12.0	8.80
Stomach	0.64	3.77
Lung	3.53	1.96
Breast	1.60	0.35
Leukaemia	0.87	0.91
All cancers	12.9	9.71

TABLE 4.2
Estimates of radiation-induced cancer deaths in a UK population, based on multiplicative and additive (NIH) models for the transfer of risks across populations and a relative risk projection over time (based on Land and Sinclair[34])

Note Exposure to high doses at high dose rates.

30 The epidemiological information available to decide how risks should be transferred across populations is limited. However, that which is available will now be reviewed according to cancer type, along with information from animal studies.

Breast cancer

31 Land *et al*[35] conducted an early parallel analysis of breast cancer incidence among the Japanese atomic bomb survivors and women in North America irradiated for medical reasons (ie X-ray therapy for acute postpartum mastitis in New York State and multiple fluoroscopies for tuberculosis in Massachusetts). At the time of that analysis the data appeared to be consistent with the constancy of absolute rather than relative risks across populations. The BEIR V Committee re-examined the incidence data for these cohorts, based on longer follow-ups[3]. However, as pointed out in paragraph 22, the BEIR V analysis was invalidated by the use of an incorrect version of the Japanese incidence data[30]. This problem did not affect the BEIR V comparison of the breast cancer mortality in the LSS and among Canadian tuberculosis patients given chest fluoroscopies. The excess relative risk per unit dose in the Japanese cohort was two to three times that in the Canadian cohort (excluding patients in Nova Scotia), whereas the absolute risk coefficient in the former cohort was less than that in the latter cohort (although it was not stated by how much)[3]; neither of these differences attained statistical significance.

32   Since the BEIR V preference for the transfer of breast cancer relative risks across populations was based largely on its analysis of the incidence data, judgement on this issue may have to be suspended pending the completion of a new analysis of the incidence data[30]. It should be noted that a separate analysis within the cohort of Japanese atomic bomb survivors suggests that the effect on breast cancer risk of radiation and reproductive factors such as age at first full-term pregnancy and number of births is multiplicative[36]. However, since the variation in baseline rates between populations might well be due largely to factors other than reproductive history, it may be best at present to use the data from the North American studies in estimating the risk of radiation-induced breast cancer for western populations.

Stomach cancer

33   Stather *et al*[13] examined published results from the LSS in Japan[4] and the Ankylosing Spondylitis Study (ASS) in the UK[5,37]. Whilst the excess relative risk per unit dose was similar in the two studies, the annual excess absolute risk was about an order of magnitude greater in the LSS than in the ASS. The latter result reflected the much higher baseline rates for stomach cancer in Japan compared with the UK. Consequently these data provide support for the transfer of the relative risk of stomach cancer from Japan to the UK.

Lung cancer

34   Variations in baseline lung cancer rates between countries are due mainly to differences in smoking habits. Information on the joint effect of radiation and smoking is therefore of key importance in determining how radiation-induced lung cancer risks vary across populations. Kopecky *et al*[38] examined this issue using data for the Japanese atomic bomb survivors. Whilst the data were fitted well by an additive relationship for smoking and radiation, they were also consistent with a multiplicative relationship. It should also be pointed out that this analysis was based on the old T65DR dosimetry, now superseded by DS86, and involved follow-up only to the end of 1980. An analysis based on the new dosimetry and with a longer follow-up might be more informative.

35   The relationship between smoking and radon has been examined in a number of studies of miners; further details are given in paragraphs 85–87. To summarise, the data are generally not consistent with an additive effect of radon and smoking on the lung cancer risk. However, while some studies are consistent with a multiplicative

relationship[2], others are more suggestive of a submultiplicative relationship; eg the study of Czech uranium miners by Sevc et al[39]. Further light may be shed on this topic by a parallel analysis of miner data sets that is currently being performed under the coordination of the National Cancer Institute in the USA. However, it should be borne in mind that the interaction with smoking may differ between low LET radiation and radon.

Skin cancer

36   The study of children in the USA (New York) treated with X-rays for ringworm of the scalp[32] indicated that the absolute radiation-induced risk depended on ethnic origin. Although 25% of the study population were black, none developed skin cancer; the excess risk was confined to whites in the population. The study of children in Israel irradiated for ringworm of the scalp[9] gave an absolute risk coefficient that fell between that for whites and the zero risk for blacks found in the American study. However, the excess relative risk from the Israeli study (0.7 Gy^{-1}) was similar to that from the American study (0.62 Gy^{-1}). These results provide support for the multiplicative transfer of radiation-induced skin cancer risks across populations.

Thyroid cancer

37   Data on thyroid cancer incidence among children in Israel irradiated for ringworm of the scalp[8] and children in New York State (USA) irradiated for enlarged thymus[31] were analysed by the BEIR V Committee[3]. The excess relative risk per unit dose in the former cohort was found to be about 2.7 times that in the latter cohort, although this difference was not statistically significant. However, there were also indications of differences in the absolute risk between the Israeli study and both the New York State study and some other studies in the USA[40]. Within the Israeli study itself, the relative risk appeared to be higher for those born in Israel than in Asia or North Africa[3]. In estimating thyroid cancer risks for a western population, it may therefore be best in view of the uncertainties in the transfer of risks across populations to use data from the USA.

Animal studies

38   Storer et al[41] studied the relationship between the radiation-induced cancer risk and the baseline cancer risk in mice. They examined cancer rates in mice of different strains and sexes, between which the baseline risks for individual cancer types varied widely. It was found that for most cancers the data were inconsistent with the constancy of absolute risk coefficients across strains and sexes. However, models under which the relative risks are constant provided better fits and were generally consistent with the data. This gives support to the transfer of relative risks across populations, at least when differences in baseline rates are the result of genetic differences in susceptibility.

Conclusions on transfer of risks across populations

39   The available data generally favour the transfer of relative rather than absolute risks across populations. However, there are still uncertainties, particularly for breast and lung cancer, although the position concerning the former cancer type may become clearer when a parallel anaysis of relevant data sets has been completed. Further parallel analyses of different epidemiological data sets and investigations into how radiation interacts with other factors to affect cancer risks would be highly useful.

40   The approach taken here to estimate risks for a UK population is to transfer risks multiplicatively from Japan or, if possible, use data from a western population as in the case of bone, breast, liver, skin and thyroid cancer. The results in Table 4.2 based on the multiplicative model and on the 'NIH' model (additive transfer across populations, relative risk projection over time)[34] illustrate the importance of the method of transferring risks on the estimates for particular cancers. However, unlike ICRP[15], the risks under multiplicative and additive transfers across populations will not be averaged, but rather preference will be given to the multiplicative model.

Effects of sex and age at exposure

Sex

41   For certain types of cancer, differences between sexes in the baseline cancer risk are paralleled in the radiation-induced risk. For example, absolute risk coefficients for leukaemia in males from the LSS are higher than the corresponding values for females, whereas the relative risk coefficients are similar for the two sexes[4]. Furthermore, among children irradiated for enlarged thymus[31], the relative risk coefficients for thyroid cancer were similar across sexes, whereas the absolute risk coefficients were about two to three times greater for females than for males.

42   For other cancers there are indications of higher relative risks for females than for males in the LSS, whereas the absolute excess risks appear to be similar across sexes. In the analyses by the BEIR V Committee of the LSS data[3], the excess relative risk per unit dose for digestive cancers was estimated to be 74% greater for females than for males, while for respiratory cancers the relative risk coefficients were 103% greater for females than for males. However, these differences may represent the effect of other factors. In particular, Kopecky *et al*[38] showed in an analysis of earlier data that, under an additive model for the joint effect of radiation and smoking (see paragraph 34), adjustment for smoking reduces the difference between sexes in the lung cancer relative risk in the LSS.

43   As a general principle, it is advisable to allow for any differences between sexes in constructing models for radiation-induced cancer risks, so as to avoid any possible confounding effect of sex. This principle has been followed in the derivation of the cancer risk estimates described in paragraphs 57–73 below.

Age at exposure

44   A common feature of studies in radiation epidemiology such as the LSS is that the relative risk tends to decrease with increasing age at exposure. This feature was incorporated in the models developed by the BEIR V Committee for leukaemia and for solid cancers, with the exception of respiratory cancers. Even in the latter case, Kopecky *et al*[38] showed that adjustment of smoking using an additive model reveals a decreasing relative risk with increasing age at exposure for lung cancer based on earlier LSS data. Similar patterns have also been seen, for example, for solid cancers in the ASS[5], for breast cancers among patients with medical exposures[6,28,29], and even within the age at exposure range 1–15 years for thyroid cancer among children in Israel irradiated for ringworm of the scalp[8].

45   There are also indications that age at exposure may affect the temporal pattern of risk. As mentioned in paragraph 17, the decrease in the leukaemia risk with time since exposure seems to be slower for those aged more than 20 years at exposure than for

those at younger ages. For the grouping of all cancers other than leukaemia, the analysis of the LSS data by Little and Charles[42] gave some suggestion of a slight decrease in the relative risk over time for those aged less than 20 years at exposure but a slight increase over time in the relative risk for those exposed at older ages. This is consistent with the age and time variation in risks predicted under a multistage model with radiation acting at an early stage (see paragraphs 12–15). The evidence for a temporal decrease in the relative risk in the LSS seems to be strongest for those aged less than 10 years at exposure although based on a small number of deaths[4]. The future temporal pattern in risk for those exposed early in life is particularly important for the calculation of the lifetime cancer risk since, within the LSS, this group is only now reaching the ages at which solid cancers tend to occur. Whilst the excess risk expressed so far for this group is low in absolute terms, it could increase by an order of magnitude if the relative risk to date were to remain constant until the end of life[43].

46   It is therefore important to take account of age at exposure in modelling radiation-induced cancer risks. However, it should be recognised that the data available for individual cancer types may not always be strong enough to provide stable estimates of risks based on fine groupings for age at exposure. In particular, as stated above, there is still relatively little information on the risks of solid cancers for those exposed early in life in the LSS. An example of an unstable estimate of the relative risk is that for colon cancer at ages at exposure less than 20 years in the LSS[4]. One method of improving precision is to fit a model under which the relative risk varies as a smooth or piecewise-smooth function of age at exposure (as in BEIR V[3]), so as to combine information across wider ranges of ages. However, there is a need to balance the wish to improve precision against the possibility of introducing bias owing to an incorrect specification for the variation in risk with age at exposure.

Extrapolation to low doses and low dose rates

Dose–response analyses

47   One of the main epidemiological sources of information on the shape of the dose–response relationship for radiation-induced cancer is the study of the Japanese atomic bomb survivors. Pierce and Vaeth[44] examined data from the follow-up to 1985, based on the DS86 dosimetry. In their analyses those with shielded kerma estimates in excess of 4 Gy were excluded, in view of an apparent levelling-off in the dose response beyond 4 Gy that may be associated with errors in the estimates of such high doses or with cell killing. Pierce and Vaeth estimated a linear extrapolation overestimation factor (LEOF), ie the ratio of the slope from the fit of a linear dose–response model to the slope at low doses from fitting a linear–quadratic model. For the grouping of all cancers other than leukaemia, the maximum likelihood estimate of LEOF was 1.2, with a 90% confidence interval (CI) ranging from less than 1 to 2.3. However, after adjusting for random errors in the dose estimates, the best estimate of LEOF was 1.4 with a 90% CI ranging from less than 1 to more than 3.1. Thus the data for all cancers other than leukaemia are fitted well by a linear dose–response model, although they are also consistent with a linear–quadratic model for which the linear extrapolation overestimation factor is between 2 and 3.

48   For leukaemia, the maximum likelihood estimate for the LEOF from the Japanese data was 1.6 (90% CI 1.0 to at least 3.1) without adjustment for random dosimetry errors and 2.0 (90% CI 1.1 to at least 3.1) with adjustment for these errors. Thus these data suggest that a linear dose–response model does not provide a good fit and that a linear–quadratic model with a linear extrapolation overestimation factor of about 2 is to be preferred.

49   Dose–response analyses have also been performed for some groups with medical exposures. Boice *et al*[29] studied the relationship between the risk of breast cancer and dose for women in Massachusetts (USA) given multiple chest X-ray fluoroscopies. For this study doses were mostly in the range 0–3 Gy. A linear dose–response model was found to provide as good a fit as a linear–quadratic model to these data, whereas a purely quadratic model did not fit well. In the study of Canadian tuberculosis patients given fluoroscopies, Miller *et al*[6] showed that a linear dose–response model fitted well to the data on breast cancer among patients other than those in Nova Scotia. (For the Nova Scotia patients, who generally received higher doses, the dose–response relationship was also consistent with linearity, but with a steeper slope than for other Canadian patients.) Among women given radiotherapy for cervical cancer, the risk of leukaemia increased with dose up to 4 Gy in a manner consistent with linearity, although the data were also consistent with a quadratic dose response; beyond 4 Gy the risk decreased, probably as a result of cell killing[45]. At lower doses, Ron *et al*[8] found that the risk of thyroid cancer among children in Israel irradiated for *tinea capitis* (ringworm of the scalp) was consistent with a linear dose–response relationship, based on doses that were mostly less than 0.15 Gy.

50   To conclude, investigations of dose–response relationships in epidemiological studies show that, after excluding very high doses if necessary, the data are generally consistent with linearity. However, other forms of model are also consistent with the data; in particular, linear–quadratic models under which the slope of the dose–response decreases with decreasing dose. In the case of leukaemia among the Japanese atomic bomb survivors, a model of the latter type was found on statistical grounds to provide a significantly better fit than a linear model.

Low dose rate studies

51   Epidemiological studies of populations exposed at low dose rates are reviewed in Appendix B. By themselves these studies do not have enough statistical power to allow risks associated with this type of exposure to be estimated precisely. There is also the problem that some of these studies, particularly those involving geographical correlations, may have been affected by confounding factors. Whilst there are statistical uncertainties of several-fold, the results from studies that have been performed on an individual basis, such as those of radiation workers (see, for example, references 10 and 46), are generally consistent with the risk estimates of ICRP[15], which were based on high dose rate studies to which a DDREF (dose and dose rate effectiveness factor) of 2 was applied.

Choice of DDREF

52   Analyses of dose–response relationships for solid tumours in epidemiological studies are, as indicated in paragraphs 47–50, generally consistent with linearity but also with a reduction in the slope of the dose–response curve at lower doses. For leukaemia among the Japanese atomic bomb survivors, however, the data are inconsistent with linearity and the central estimate of the factor for reduction in risk at low doses is 2.

Studies of low dose rate exposure lack sufficient statistical power to allow risks to be estimated precisely. Furthermore, it is unclear whether the value for DDREF is the same for all organs. Consequently, as pointed out in Chapter 3, account needs to be taken of information from animal and *in vitro* experiments in deriving an overall value for DDREF. Although these experiments suggest values in the range from about 1 to more than 10, the human data suggest values at the lower end of this range for extrapolation to low doses. In particular, as indicated above, the human low dose rate studies are consistent with DDREF values in the region of 2. Therefore, as suggested in Chapter 3, a DDREF of 2 is used here for the purposes of estimating cancer risks associated with exposures to low doses or at low dose rates (as defined in Chapter 8), based on results from epidemiological studies of exposures to high doses at high dose rates.

Life table calculations

53   Different measures of risk or detriment have been calculated in the past, based on models developed for radiation-induced cancer risks. The approach taken here, as in UNSCEAR[1] and Stather *et al*[13], involves the calculation of the number of attributable radiation-induced cancer deaths following exposure of a standard population. It should be emphasised that this quantity, which was also calculated by ICRP[15], differs from the number of excess cancer deaths in a population, as used by the BEIR IV and V Committees[2,3]. The latter quantity excludes that proportion among those who die of a radiation-induced cancer who would have otherwise died from a 'naturally occurring' cancer at a later time. These radiation-induced cancers do not add to the number of excess cancers, but they are attributable to radiation and contribute to the expected years of life lost. For all cancers, the number of excess deaths calculated under the BEIR approach is about 20%–25% less than the number of radiation-induced deaths presented below. Aside from numbers of deaths, other aspects that bear upon the detriment from radiation-induced cancer are the years of life lost and occurrence of non-fatal cancers[47,90]. These quantities, along with a component representing hereditary disease, have been incorporated in the measure of detriment developed by ICRP[15].

54   Features of the baseline population to which the risk models are applied in the life table calculations can influence the values calculated[90]. Of particular importance are the baseline rates for the cancer in question (if a relative risk model is being used), the baseline rates for all causes of death (which influence the probability that any excess radiation risk will be expressed) and the age structure of the population at the time of exposure. To allow comparison with Stather *et al*[13], the same approach will be taken here. The 1985 life table and baseline cancer rates for England and Wales[48] will be used, and the risks associated with a single exposure to

(i)   the general population of all ages,
(ii)   a working population of ages 18–64 years,

will be evaluated. It should be emphasised that in the case of leukaemia, baseline rates that exclude chronic lymphatic leukaemia (CLL) will be utilised, since CLL does not appear to be radiation inducible. This approach is in contrast to that of BEIR[3] which applied its time varying relative risk model to baseline rates that included CLL[49]. Consequently, as pointed out by Muirhead[43], the risk estimates for leukaemia presented by BEIR are too high.

55   In order to estimate the risks of non-fatal cancers, the approach that will be taken involves multiplying the risk of mortality for the cancer in question by $(1 - F)/F$, where F is the proportion of the cancers induced that prove to be fatal averaged over all ages. This is the same approach as that of ICRP[15] for estimating the number of non-fatal cancers, although the values for F used here are specific to a UK population.

56   The calculations of cancer risk presented here are based on the effect of a single exposure, averaged over a population of various ages. In addition to this type of calculation, the BEIR V Committee[3] estimated the effect of continuous exposure at a constant dose rate either over a lifetime or throughout working life. For doses that are sufficiently low not to have an appreciable effect on all-cause annual mortality rates, both types of calculation can be related to weighted averages or sums of the age-specific risks associated with a single exposure. In the case of a single exposure of a population of various ages, the weights used in averaging represent the proportions in the different age groups. For a continuous exposure, however, the weights used in summing risks across exposure ages represent the probability of surviving to a given age. For a population whose age structure is reasonably constant over time, the two sets of weights will be similar, and so the two types of risks can be related in a simple manner. However, if the weights differ, owing to changes in the age structure of the population over time, then the relationship between these two measures is more complex.

RISK ESTIMATES FOR A UK POPULATION

Fatal cancers

57   From the data sources and risk models summarised in Table 4.3, Table 4.4 gives estimates for numbers of radiation-induced deaths in a UK population of all ages and both sexes, calculated on the basis of the life tables described above. Corresponding values for a working population exposed at ages 18–64 years are given in Table 4.5; this age range coincides with that used by ICRP[15]. Estimates associated with both exposure to high doses at high dose rates and exposure to low doses or low dose rates are presented in these tables, based on a DDREF of 2 (see paragraph 52). For each cancer type estimates were made on the basis of both the projection of risks over an entire lifetime and up to 40 years following exposure, ie the follow-up time for the Japanese survivors[4]. For some solid cancers, estimates based on Armitage–Doll multistage models were also calculated to illustrate the use of mechanistic models (Table 4.6).

58   Further details of the models listed in Table 4.3 and of the interpretation of the results in Tables 4.4–4.6 are given below for each cancer type.

Leukaemia

59   The BEIR V relative risk model for leukaemia, derived from analysis of the LSS data[3], was applied to UK baseline rates. Under this model, the relative risk decreases with both age at exposure and time since exposure. Since this model is applied to baseline rates excluding chronic lymphatic leukaemia, unlike the BEIR V report (see paragraph 54), the low dose/low dose rate lifetime risk for a general population in Table 4.4, namely $0.6 \ 10^{-2} \ Sv^{-1}$, is less than that calculated by BEIR V.

60   The lifetime risk is slightly greater than the risk to 40 years since, as pointed out in paragraph 17, the BEIR V model does predict a small risk beyond this time. The high

TABLE 4.3 Data sources and risk models used to produce estimates of radiation-induced cancer deaths in a UK population

Cancer type	Data source	Risk model
Leukaemia	Atomic bomb survivors	Relative risk varying over time and constant across populations (BEIR V[3])
Breast	North American patients	Relative risk constant across time and populations (Gilbert[50])
Lung	Atomic bomb survivors	Relative risk varying over time, constant across populations (BEIR V[3])
Thyroid	North American patients	Absolute risk constant across time and populations (NCRP[51])
Bone	German patients with intakes of ^{224}Ra (BEIR IV[2])	Absolute risk constant over period 2–40 years following exposure, and constant across populations
Liver	European patients given Thorotrast, (BEIR IV[2])	Absolute risk constant across time and populations
Colon	Atomic bomb survivors	Relative risk constant across time and populations (BEIR V[3])
Stomach	Atomic bomb survivors	Relative risk constant across time and populations (BEIR V[3])
Skin	North American children irradiated for ringworm of the scalp (BEIR III[12])	Absolute risk constant across time and populations
Remainder	Atomic bomb survivors	Relative risk constant across time and populations (BEIR V[3])

dose/dose rate risk to 40 years in Table 4.4 is in turn about 30% greater than the corresponding value in Stather *et al*[13], since the latter value was based on published data from the LSS for doses in the range 0–6 Gy (Shimizu *et al*[4]), whereas the BEIR V Committee was able to derive a model based on detailed data for the 0–4 Gy range (see also paragraph 47). For a worker population (Table 4.5), the risk is reduced slightly relative to a general population owing to the exclusion of children.

TABLE 4.4
Estimates of radiation-induced fatal cancer risks in a UK population of all ages and both sexes

| Cancer type | Deaths (10^{-2} Sv^{-1}) | | | |
| | Lifetime projection | | Risk up to 40 years following exposure | |
	HDR[a]	LDR[b]	HDR[a]	LDR[b]
Leukaemia	1.2	0.60	1.11	0.55
Breast	1.1	0.55	0.42	0.21
Lung	2.2	1.09	1.67	0.83
Thyroid	0.067	0.034	0.044	0.022
Bone	0.10	0.05	0.10	0.05
Liver	0.30	0.15	0.16	0.08
Colon	1.03	0.51	0.19	0.09
Stomach	0.84	0.42	0.14	0.07
Skin	0.032	0.016	0.02	0.01
Remainder[c]	4.89	2.45	1.01	0.51
Total	11.8	5.9	4.9	2.4

Notes
(a) Exposure to high doses at high dose rates..
(b) Exposure to low doses or at low dose rates, based on a DDREF of 2.
(c) Within the remainder, the results presented by Land and Sinclair[34] yield the following risks under a relative risk lifetime projection for LDR exposure: bladder – 0.48 10^{-2} Sv^{-1}; oesophagus – 0.24 10^{-2} Sv^{-1}; ovary – 0.30 10^{-2} Sv^{-1}.

Breast cancer

61   In view both of the problems with the BEIR V analysis that were highlighted in paragraphs 22, 31 and 32 and of the current uncertainty in how to transfer risks across populations, data from studies of patients in North America have been used. In particular, the model described by Gilbert[50] has been utilised for high dose and high dose rate exposure, under which the relative risk remains constant with time since exposure (following a latent period of 10 years) and for which the excess relative risk for those exposed prior to age 20 years (namely 1.03 Sv^{-1}) is larger than that (0.42 Sv^{-1}) for those exposed at older ages. This is the same model as used by Stather *et al*[13]. For a

general population, the projected lifetime risk at high doses/high dose rates (1.1 10^{-2} Sv^{-1}) is larger than the corresponding value based on the BEIR V model (0.4 10^{-2} Sv^{-1}; Muirhead[43]); as pointed out in paragraphs 22, 31 and 32, the variation in relative risk over time under the BEIR V model seems, at least in part, to be artefactual. The high dose rate lifetime risk in Table 4.4 is also substantially higher than the value of 0.25 10^{-2} Sv^{-1} quoted by Land and Sinclair[34] for a Japanese population based on the LSS data. As was emphasised in paragraphs 28 and 29, baseline breast cancer rates are higher in the UK than in Japan.

| | Deaths (10^{-2} Sv^{-1}) | | | |
| | Lifetime projection | | Risk up to 40 years following exposure | |
Cancer type	HDR[a]	LDR[b]	HDR[a]	LDR[b]
Leukaemia	0.97	0.48	0.90	0.45
Breast	0.87	0.43	0.51	0.26
Lung	2.79	1.39	2.34	1.17
Thyroid	0.047	0.023	0.036	0.018
Bone	0.10	0.05	0.10	0.05
Liver	0.30	0.15	0.16	0.08
Colon	0.79	0.39	0.24	0.12
Stomach	0.64	0.32	0.19	0.10
Skin	0.028	0.014	0.022	0.011
Remainder[c]	3.53	1.76	1.45	0.72
Total	10.1	5.0	5.9	3.0

TABLE 4.5 *Estimates of radiation-induced fatal cancer risks in a UK working population aged 18–64 years (both sexes)*

Notes
(a) Exposure to high doses at high dose rates..
(b) Exposure to low doses or at low dose rates, based on a DDREF of 2.
(c) Within the remainder, the results presented by Land and Sinclair[34] yield the following risks under a relative risk lifetime projection for LDR exposure: bladder – 0.52 10^{-2} Sv^{-1}; oesophagus – 0.26 10^{-2} Sv^{-1}; ovary – 0.33 10^{-2} Sv^{-1}.

Lung cancer

62   The values in Tables 4.4 and 4.5 for lung cancer following high dose and high dose rate exposure are based on applying the BEIR V time varying relative risk model for respiratory cancer (see equation A3 in Appendix A) to baseline lung cancer rates. The analyses in Appendix A show that a model of this type provides a good fit to the LSS data for lung cancer alone. Whilst there are only slight indications in the LSS of a decrease in the relative risk over time, there is stronger evidence from the Ankylosing

Spondylitis Study (ASS) (see paragraph 21). It is noteworthy that the lifetime risk under this model ($1.09\ 10^{-2}\ Sv^{-1}$ for low dose/low dose rate exposure of a general population) is only slightly greater than the risk up to 40 years following exposure ($0.83\ 10^{-2}\ Sv^{-1}$), suggesting that little risk will be expressed beyond 40 years. Furthermore, the projections under this model are similar to those under the Armitage–Doll multistage model (Table 4.6), which also predicts a decrease in relative risk over time. Since the effect of this decrease on the lifetime risk is strongest for those exposed at the youngest ages, and, under the BEIR V model, the relative risk does not decrease with increasing age at exposure (unlike most other solid cancers), the risk for a population of all ages in Table 4.4 is smaller than the corresponding value for a working population in Table 4.5.

TABLE 4.6
Illustrative application
of Armitage–Doll
multistage models in
estimating radiation-
induced fatal cancer
risks in a UK
population of all ages
and both sexes

Cancer type	Deaths ($10^{-2}\ Sv^{-1}$)	
	Lifetime projection	
	HDR[a]	LDR[b]
Lung[c]	2.4	1.2
Colon[d]	0.89	0.45
Stomach[d]	0.49	0.25
All except leukaemia, bone, breast, colon, lung, skin, stomach and thyroid[e]	4.1	2.1

Notes
(a) Exposure to high doses at high dose rates..
(b) Exposure to low doses or at low dose rates, based on a DDREF of 2.
(c) Based on a 5-stage model fitted to the LSS data under which radiation acts at the 5th stage for males and the 2nd stage for females (see Appendix A).
(d) Based on a model under which radiation acts at the 2nd out of a total of 5 stages (see Appendix A).
(e) Based on a model under which radiation acts at the 1st out of a total of 5 stages (see Appendix A).

Thyroid cancer

63   The high dose rate values for thyroid cancer in Tables 4.4 and 4.5 are based on the age-specific absolute risk coefficients quoted by NCRP[51]. These risk coefficients were derived from a review of studies of young people in North America who received external exposures for medical reasons. As suggested in paragraph 37, it may be best to use data from North America in estimating risks for a western population, in view of the uncertainties on how to transfer thyroid cancer risks from other populations. In line with the study of children in New York State irradiated for enlarged thymus (see paragraph 25), an absolute risk model for projection over time is used with a latent period of 5 years and results are quoted in Tables 4.4 and 4.5 for expression both over a lifetime and up to 40 years following exposure. The risks of mortality were derived on the assumption that 10% of radiation-induced thyroid cancer cases are fatal (NCRP[51]). It should be emphasised that a DDREF of 2 has been applied to obtain the risks for low dose/low dose rate exposure (ie $3.4\ 10^{-4}\ Sv^{-1}$ for a general population), in contrast to ICRP which did not apply a DDREF[15].

Bone cancer

64   The risks for low dose rates in Tables 4.4 and 4.5 are based on the follow-up of German patients with intakes of radium-224 (BEIR IV[2]). With a quality factor for alpha radiation of 20, the annual absolute excess risk is estimated as $1.7 \ 10^{-5} \ y^{-1} \ Gy^{-1}$ (low LET, low dose rate). An absolute risk projection over time is assumed, based on an expression period of 2–40 years following exposure. The risk from low LET exposure at high dose rates is taken to be twice that at low dose rates. The value of $5 \ 10^{-4} \ Sv^{-1}$ in Table 4.4 for low dose rate exposure is consistent with that given by ICRP[15] for a general population.

Liver cancer

65   The risks for low dose rate exposure are based on the review by the BEIR IV Committee[2] of studies of European patients (mainly in Germany as well as in Portugal) given Thorotrast, an X-ray contrast medium used formerly in diagnostic radiology. A quality factor for alpha radiation of 20 is assumed. The excess risk is taken to commence 20 years after exposure and to continue either until the end of life or up to 40 years following exposure[2]. The risk from low LET exposure at high dose rates is assumed to be twice that at low dose rates. The value of $1.5 \ 10^{-3} \ Sv^{-1}$ in Table 4.4 for low dose rate exposure from BEIR IV coincides with that given by ICRP[15] for a general population.

Colon cancer

66   The values in Tables 4.4 and 4.5 for colon cancer following high dose and high dose rate exposure are based on applying the BEIR V relative risk model for digestive cancers (see equation A4 in Appendix A) to baseline colon cancer rates. Under the BEIR V model, which was derived from analysis of the LSS data, the relative risk remains constant over time (following a latent period of 10 years) and decreases with increasing age at exposure. For a general population the risk projected to arise over a lifetime (ie $0.51 \ 10^{-2} \ Sv^{-1}$ for low dose/low dose rate exposure) is over five times greater than that up to 40 years following exposure (Table 4.4). This serves to emphasise the importance for estimating lifetime risks for the continued follow-up of those atomic bomb survivors exposed when young. The risks in Table 4.6 predicted under the fit of an Armitage–Doll multistage model (see Appendix A) are not too dissimilar from those based on a lifetime relative risk projection.

Stomach cancer

67   The values in Tables 4.4 and 4.5 for stomach cancer following high dose and high dose rate exposure are based on applying the BEIR V relative risk model for digestive cancers (see equation A4 in Appendix A) to baseline stomach cancer rates. Under the BEIR V model, the relative risk remains constant with time since exposure (following a latent period of 10 years) and decreases with increasing age at exposure. It is shown in Appendix A that a model of this type provides a good fit to the LSS data for stomach cancer alone. Also, it was pointed out in paragraph 33 that comparisons of the LSS and ASS data support the transfer of relative risks of stomach cancer from Japan to the UK and so support values towards the lower end of the range in Table 4.2. As with colon cancer, the risks in a general population based on a lifetime projection (ie $0.42 \ 10^{-2} \ Sv^{-1}$ for low dose/low dose rate exposure) are substantially higher than those up to 40 years following exposure (Table 4.4), so emphasising the uncertainty in lifetime risks for those irradiated when young. The risk in the general population under the multistage model (Table 4.6) lies between the lifetime relative risk projection and the risk to 40 years in Table 4.4.

Skin cancer

68   For high dose rate whole-body exposure, the annual absolute excess risk for skin cancer incidence has been taken to be $1 \ 10^{-3} \ y^{-1} \ Gy^{-1}$ (low LET), as derived by BEIR[12] on the basis of the follow-up of North American children irradiated for ringworm of the scalp. It has been assumed that 1% of these cases will be fatal, and that the absolute risks remain constant over time following a 10 year latent period. As was stated in paragraph 26 there is uncertainty about the temporal pattern of radiation-induced skin cancer. The risk of fatal skin cancer given in Table 4.4 for low dose rate exposure of a general population ($1.6 \ 10^{-4} \ Sv^{-1}$) is similar to that quoted by ICRP[15].

Remainder

69   For exposure to high doses at high dose rates, the BEIR V relative risk model for the grouping of all cancers other than leukaemia, breast, respiratory and digestive cancers (see equation A5 in Appendix A) was applied to baseline rates for all cancers other than those listed above (with the exception of liver cancer, which was included in the calculation because it was not possible to specify a separate model for it). The resultant risks, with the values for liver cancer subtracted, are shown in Tables 4.4 and 4.5. Since the form of the BEIR V model is such that the relative risks are highest for ages at exposure of less than 10 years and remain constant with time since exposure (following a 10 year latent period), there is a large difference between the risk projected over a lifetime and that up to 40 years following exposure in the general population (Table 4.4). As with other solid cancers, this reflects uncertainty in lifetime risks for those exposed when young. Consequently the difference between the lifetime projection and the risk to 40 years is not as great for those exposed at ages 18–64 years (Table 4.5). It is noteworthy that the risk estimated in the general population under a multistage model (Table 4.6) lies towards the upper end of the range between the lifetime projection and the risk to 40 years in Table 4.4 for the sum of remainder and liver cancers.

70   It should be pointed out the remainder grouping in Tables 4.4 and 4.5 includes bladder, ovary and oesophagus, for which ICRP derived specific cancer risks[15]. Whilst analysis of the Japanese survivor data[4] does show statistically significant trends with dose in the risk for each of these cancers, the data are still sparse and there are uncertainties in attempting to specify risk models for these cancers individually. It was because of uncertainties of this type that the BEIR V Committee generally analysed the Japanese data in terms of groupings of cancers rather than individually. Results presented by Land and Sinclair[34] indicate that for exposure of a general UK population, the sum of the lifetime risks for bladder, ovary and oesophagus is about 40% of the value for remainder organs in Table 4.4.

Total cancer risk

71   For a general UK population the total risk of radiation-induced cancer is estimated as $11.8 \ 10^{-2} \ Sv^{-1}$ for exposure to low LET radiation at high doses and high dose rates, and as $5.9 \ 10^{-2} \ Sv^{-1}$ for low dose or low dose rate exposures (Table 4.4). The latter value is somewhat greater than the value of $5 \ 10^{-2} \ Sv^{-1}$ quoted by ICRP[15], owing to some differences in the models used and to higher baseline cancer rates in the UK compared

with a world average used by ICRP. Furthermore, the above risk for high dose and high dose rate exposure is greater than that given by Muirhead[43] based on applying the BEIR V models to a UK population, since the BEIR V model for breast cancer has not been used here for the reasons given in paragraphs 22, 31 and 32. It should be emphasised that the risk to 40 years following exposure is estimated to be 2.4×10^{-2} Sv^{-1} for low dose/low dose rate exposure, ie about 40% of that predicted over a lifetime. This difference is due to uncertainty about the future pattern of risk for those exposed when young. In particular, Table 4.7 shows that for those irradiated in the first 10 years of life, the risk based on a lifetime projection is an order of magnitude greater than that estimated until 40 years following exposure. This table also shows that whereas the total cancer risk predicted over a lifetime increases monotonically with decreasing age at exposure, the risk to 40 years following exposure is greatest for those irradiated at ages 50–59 years. Furthermore the variation with age at exposure is not as great for the risk to 40 years as for the lifetime projected risk. These results emphasise the importance of continued follow-up of groups such as those Japanese survivors exposed early in life. Table 4.8 shows that the total cancer risk is generally similar for males and females, although that for females is slightly larger for exposure early in life.

Age at exposure (years)	Deaths (10^{-2} Sv^{-1})				
	Lifetime projection		Risk up to 40 years following exposure		
	HDR[a]	LDR[b]		HDR[a]	LDR[b]
0–9	22.3	11.1		2.3	1.2
10–19	19.8	9.9		3.7	1.8
20–29	13.1	6.6		3.8	1.9
30–39	8.9	4.5		5.6	2.8
40–49	8.4	4.2		7.5	3.8
50–59	8.0	4.0		7.9	4.0
60–69	6.2	3.1		6.2	3.1
70–79	3.3	1.6		3.3	1.6
80+	1.5	0.75		1.5	0.75

TABLE 4.7
Estimates of radiation-induced fatal cancer risks in a UK population of both sexes, according to age at exposure

Notes
(a) Exposure to high doses at high dose rates..
(b) Exposure to low doses or at low dose rates, based on a DDREF of 2.

72   For a population with low dose/low dose rate exposure at ages 18–64 years, the risk predicted over a lifetime is 5.0×10^{-2} Sv^{-1} (Table 4.5). This is also somewhat higher than the ICRP value for a working population of 4.0×10^{-2} Sv^{-1} for the same reasons as above. Since those at young ages are excluded from this population, the difference between the risk predicted over a lifetime and that up to 40 years following exposure (ie 3.0×10^{-2} Sv^{-1} for low dose/low dose rate exposure) is less than that for a general population.

73   The risks given in Table 4.4 and 4.5 for low dose/low dose rate exposure are generally higher than the corresponding values given by Stather *et al*[13], ie total lifetime cancer risks of 4.5 10^{-2} Sv^{-1} for a general UK population and 3.4 10^{-2} Sv^{-1} for a working population. This is due primarily to the use here of a DDREF of 2 for all organs whereas Stather *et al* used a DDREF of 3 for all organs other than breast (for which the DDREF was taken as 2). There are also some slight changes owing to differences in the models for age-specific and sex-specific risks and in the definition of a working population (ages 18–64 years here, rather than 20–64 years).

TABLE 4.8
Estimates of radiation-induced fatal cancer risks in a UK population, according to sex and age at exposure

Age at exposure (years)	Deaths* (10^{-2} Sv^{-1})	
	Male	Female
0–9	10.3	12.0
10–19	9.0	10.8
20–29	6.1	7.0
30–39	4.3	4.6
40–49	4.2	4.2
50–59	4.2	3.8
60–69	3.3	2.9
70–79	1.7	1.6
80+	0.8	0.7
Population-weighted average	5.8	5.9

*Lifetime projection for exposure to low doses or at low dose rates, based on a DDREF of 2.

Non-fatal cancers

74   In estimating the detriment associated with radiation exposure, account needs to be taken of aspects other than cancer mortality. One of these aspects is the induction of non-fatal cancers. For the general population of England and Wales data on the fatality of specific cancer types have been published by the Office of Population Censuses and Surveys[52]. Restricting attention to cancers that are radiation-inducible alters some of these values. For example, the fatality rate for leukaemia is increased when the chronic lymphatic subtype (which does not appear to be radiation-inducible) is excluded; however, the 99% fatality quoted by ICRP[15] seems to be too high, given the improvements in the treatment of childhood leukaemia in recent years. Another example concerns thyroid cancer, for which radiation-inducible types appear to have lower fatality than other types[51].

75   Table 4.9 gives estimates for fatality for radiation-induced cancers, based on OPCS[52] and ICRP[53]. These values are the same as those quoted by Stather *et al*[13]. In particular, it has been assumed that 90% (rather than 99%, as in ICRP[15]) of radiation-induced leukaemias are fatal. Whilst ideally these fatality rates could be subdivided to reflect age-dependent differences in survival, the values in Table 4.9 give an indication of the pattern in survival averaged over a population of all ages. In particular, summing over all cancer types, the number of non-fatal radiation-induced cancers is estimated to be about two-thirds the number of fatal cancers.

Aggregated detriment: tissue weighting factors

76   To ensure that the combination of different doses to several organs correlates with the total radiation detriment, tissue weighting factors (w_T) are defined that broadly

Cancer type	Percentage fatal
Leukaemia	90
Breast	50
Lung	95
Thyroid	10
Bone	80
Liver	95
Colon	75
Stomach	95
Skin	1
ALL	70

TABLE 4.9
Fatality rates for radiation-induced cancers (based on OPCS[52] and ICRP[53])

represent the relative contribution of each tissue to the total detriment associated with uniform whole-body irradiation. In ICRP Publication 60[15], this weighted sum of organ doses is termed 'effective dose', replacing the quantity effective dose equivalent in the previous recommendations. Organ-specific fatal cancer risks, such as those discussed in paragraphs 59–70, are used as a basis for the w_T values, but the formulation of effective dose also includes three other components: the weighted probability of non-fatal cancers, the weighted probability of hereditary effects, and the relative length of life lost from fatal effects. To decide on appropriate values for w_T, a sensitivity analysis using two health effects models and five reference populations was carried out by ICRP[15] to provide a series of fatal cancer risk estimates that were in turn normalised, averaged, and rounded. Each organ was then allocated to one of four different weights.

77   In ICRP Publication 60, the tissue weighting factors are deliberately rounded and take account of, *inter alia*, the range of fatal cancer risks across different populations. Table 4.10 shows estimates of fatal cancer risks derived by ICRP and the Board. The figures derived by the Board do not give reason to move from the rounded w_T values recommended by ICRP for setting protection standards, eg limits and constraints. The Board's risk estimates are for use in calculating late health effects within a UK population; for example, in accident consequence assessments or in determining probability of causation.

EPIDEMIOLOGY OF EXPOSURE TO RADON

Radon and lung cancer

Studies of miners

78   The main epidemiological evidence for the role of radon exposure in the induction of lung cancer comes from a multitude of studies of miners of uranium, tin and iron ores. Details of the main studies are summarised in Table 4.11. The total number of men

TABLE 4.10
Ranges for fatal cancer probabilities

Tissue	Probability of fatal cancer[a] (10^{-2} Sv^{-1})		
	NRPB estimate	ICRP range[b]	ICRP estimate
Bone marrow	0.60	0.25–0.60	0.50
Bone surface[c]	0.05	0.05	0.05
Breast	0.55	0.07–0.55	0.20
Colon	0.51	0.32–1.79	0.85
Liver[c]	0.15	0.15	0.15
Lung	1.09	0.31–1.77	0.85
Skin[c]	0.02	0.02	0.02
Stomach	0.42	0.18–1.76	1.10
Thyroid[c]	0.03	0.08	0.08
Bladder[d]	⎫	0.11–0.58	0.30
Oesophagus[d]	⎬ 2.45	0.08–0.85	0.30
Ovary[d]	⎪	0.06–0.20	0.10
Remainder	⎭	0.45–0.97	0.50

Notes
(a) Based on low dose/low dose rate exposure of population of all ages and both sexes.
(b) Range over five populations and two models (ICRP[15]).
(c) Range not calculated.
(d) No estimate provided by NRPB in this report.

included in these studies is over 50 000, with an aggregated follow-up in excess of 800 000 person-years. The mean cumulative exposure varies widely between studies: from a few WLM at the Radium Hill mine in Australia to just under 900 WLM on the Colorado Plateau (although, for the latter study, it is possible that some of the higher exposures have been overestimated). The number of lung cancers observed in each study is substantial – generally at least 50 – and is raised to a statistically significant extent above expectation in each instance; the ratio of observed to expected values varies from just under two to about five. Furthermore, these studies show that the lung cancer risk increases with increasing cumulative exposure and, in general, it appears to be consistent with a linear relationship between exposure and risk. The exposures at which some of the studies yield a significantly raised risk, ie between 20 and 50 WLM, are only about a factor of between two and five above the mean lifetime indoor exposure received in countries such as the USA[2] and the UK, and are less than the lifetime exposure in dwellings at the UK action level (ie 75 WLM)[54]. A parallel analysis of the miner studies is currently being performed under the coordination of the American National Cancer Institute.

79   Regarding the question of whether the results have been influenced by the presence of any other carcinogens in the mines, variation in, for example, dust levels

Mine(s) (follow up period)	Reference Number	Mean WLM	Person-years	Number of lung cancer deaths	
				Observed	Expected
Colorado Plateau, USA (1951–82)	66	3 346	821	73 642	256	59.1
Ontario, Canada (1955–81)	2,56	11 076	37	217 800	87	57.9
Beaverlodge, Canada (1950–80)	67	8 487	13	114 170	65	34.2
Port Radium, Canada (1950–80)	68	2 103	144	52 930	57	24.7
Czechoslovakia (1948–80)	39	4 043	226	83 838	484	97.5
Malmberget, Sweden (1951–76)	55	1 294	94	27 397	51	14.9
New Mexico, USA (1977–85)	61	3 469	111	59 000	68	17.0
Newfoundland, Canada (1950–84)	63	1 772	383	38 500	113	21.5
Yunnan Province, China (1976–87)	59	17 143	217	175 406	981	267
Cornwall, UK (1941–86)	69	3 010	~100		105	66.6
Radium Hill, Australia (1952–87)	70	1 429	7		32	23.1

TABLE 4.11
Mortality from lung cancer among miners exposed to radon

over time has not been reflected in the miners' lung cancer rates[55], while excesses of lung cancer have still been seen at mines (eg Malmberget, Sweden) where respiratory carcinogens such as arsenic were absent. In other types of mine, such as nickel and copper mines in Ontario, no excess of lung cancer has been seen[56]. Also, it is difficult to conceive of a confounding factor that is so well correlated with radon exposure, such that it would be able to explain the exposure–response relationships seen in the different miner studies as artefacts. Further supporting evidence comes from animal studies in the USA and France, which show similar patterns of increased risks of lung cancer in rats and dogs exposed chronically to radon[2].

Estimates of lifetime risk associated with indoor radon exposure

80   Several committees have attempted to estimate the risk over a lifetime for a general population exposed in an indoor environment; in particular, ICRP[57] and the BEIR IV Committee[2]. Whilst one possible approach would involve applying a quality factor to the risks derived from low LET studies, there are difficulties owing to uncertainties concerning both the conversion of exposures to lung doses and, as pointed out in paragraph 9, the radiation quality. Consequently risk estimates have been

based generally on studies of radon-exposed miners, possibly with supplementary information from the low LET studies. Among the points that are important in producing such an estimate are the projection of doses from a mining to an indoor environment and the projection of risks from the period of follow-up in the miner studies to an entire lifetime. On the former point, the judgement of the BEIR IV Committee was that the dose per unit exposure could be taken to be the same in homes as in mines, whereas ICRP concluded that the dose per unit exposure in homes could be taken to be 80% of that in mines. More recently, a report by the American National Academy of Sciences and National Research Council[58] concluded that this factor was likely to be in the range 0.7–0.8, based on a review of factors such as aerosol characteristics and differences in breathing patterns.

81   In projecting risks over a lifetime, the ICRP preference was for a model under which the relative risk remains constant with time since exposure. Furthermore, based on information from the Japanese atomic bomb survivors, the relative risk was taken to be higher for exposures in childhood than for those later in life. The BEIR IV model, which was derived by a joint analysis of data from the Colorado Plateau, Ontario, Beaverlodge and Malmberget cohorts, allows for a decrease in the relative risk beyond 15 years following exposure and for a lower relative risk at higher attained ages.

82   Using idealised baseline rates that correspond to a world population, ICRP calculated the probability of lung cancer death due to indoor radon exposure as $2.3\ 10^{-4}$ WLM^{-1}. If, however, the ICRP model is applied to UK baseline lung cancer rates (which are higher than the world average), then the probability of radon-induced lung cancer in the UK is approximately $3.5\ 10^{-4}$ WLM^{-1}. This is the same as the value quoted in the BEIR IV report, which was based on baseline rates in the USA. While the results of the analyses of the committees are in close agreement, there are a number of areas affecting the calculation of these estimates for which some uncertainty exists.

Factors that may affect risk estimates

83   *Sex and age at exposure*   The miner studies are, by their nature, restricted to providing information on the exposure of adult males. There is therefore the question of how the risks obtained from these studies should be used to predict risks for a general population containing women and children. In assessing the risks for females, ICRP and BEIR IV both made the assumption that the relative risk is the same for both sexes. The basis for this approach was the idea that differences in the baseline lung cancer rates between sexes could be explained by differences in smoking habits and that a multiplicative model could be used to assess the joint effect of radon and smoking (see paragraphs 85–87). Under this approach, the probability of radon-induced lung cancer is higher among males than among females, reflecting the difference in baseline rates.

84   Regarding the effect of exposure to radon early in life, the only results available are from a study of Chinese tin miners, some of whom were aged less than 13 years when first exposed[59]. The relative risks for this group were slightly higher than those for first exposure at ages greater than 20 years, although the study investigators judged that the age variation in risk was not consistent. It may well be the case that information from epidemiological studies of indoor radon exposures (see paragraphs 91–93) will be required in order to obtain a better understanding of the effects of both sex and age at exposure.

85   *Joint effect of radon and smoking*   The examination of this topic by the BEIR IV Committee was based largely on data collected for the Colorado Plateau uranium miners. This analysis showed that a model under which the joint effect of radon exposure and smoking on the lung cancer risk is additive was inconsistent with the data, whereas a multiplicative model for the joint effect of radon and smoking was consistent with the data. The best fit to the data was an intermediate model, ie predicting a supra-additive but submultiplicative effect. However, because of its consistency with the Colorado Plateau data, the BEIR IV Committee adopted the multiplicative model. The consequence of this model is to predict radon-induced lung cancer risks that are about an order of magnitude greater for smokers than for non-smokers.

86   Since the BEIR IV report was published, several other publications on this topic have appeared. Roscoe *et al*[60] looked at only non-smokers among the Colorado Plateau uranium miners and noted an approximate ten-fold increase in the lung cancer risk associated with radon exposure; this value appears to be higher than the relative risk for the overall cohort of smokers and non-smokers. The study by Sevc *et al*[39] of Czech uranium miners indicated a relationship that was intermediate between additive and multiplicative, although based on only three lung cancer deaths among non-smokers. Data on Chinese tin miners[59] also suggested a submultiplicative but supra-additive model for the effect of radon and smoking. However, the study by Samet *et al*[61] on New Mexico uranium miners was consistent with a multiplicative model, as was a case–control study of Beaverlodge miners in Canada (L'Abbé *et al*[62]), although the latter authors advised caution in interpretation in view of the small numbers (46 cases, 95 controls). Among Newfoundland fluorspar miners[63] the absolute risk coefficients – compared with a general population of smokers and non-smokers – were similar for current smokers and those who had never smoked, whereas the relative risk was higher in the latter group.

87   Taken overall, the evidence from the miner studies indicates that the joint effect of radon exposure and smoking on the risk of lung cancer is greater than additive. However, while some studies are consistent with a multiplicative effect, other studies suggest that a submultiplicative model may be more appropriate, although the precise form of such a model is not entirely clear. It should be emphasised that the choice of model for the interaction between smoking and radon should not have a very large effect on the estimate of radon-induced lung cancer risk in a general population of smokers and non-smokers. The main effect of the choice of model is on how the risk is distributed between smokers and non-smokers; the use of a submultiplicative rather than a multiplicative model would narrow the difference between the radon-induced risks for smokers and non-smokers, currently estimated to differ by an order of magnitude under the latter model.

88   *Exposure rate*   Darby and Doll[64,65] have suggested that exposure rate may influence the risk of lung cancer associated with a given cumulative exposure. This was based in part on a comparison of risk coefficients obtained from studies in mines with differing mean exposure rates. In Table 4.12, which is an expanded version of a table given by Darby and Doll[65], it can be seen that there is one mine (Port Radium, with a high exposure rate) for which the relative risk was particularly low, and there are two mines (Malmberget and Beaverlodge, both with low exposure rates) for which the relative risk was particularly high. The risk coefficients for the other mines were fairly similar, taking into account the statistical uncertainties in these values, although the exposure rates in these mines covered almost as wide a range as those in the mines cited above. Darby and Doll attached particular importance to the comparison of the results for the Port Radium and Beaverlodge mines, since these mines were in the same broad geographical area and were operated by the same company. It should, however, be noted that a recent re-evaluation suggests that exposures at Beaverlodge were underestimated by about 40% on average; this information will be included in a new analysis of the Beaverlodge study[71]. The BEIR IV analysis used data for only some of the mines in Table 4.12, between which there was little evidence of heterogeneity in the risk coefficients. However, two of the mines included in the BEIR IV analysis, namely Malmberget and Beaverlodge, are those associated with the highest risk coefficients in Table 4.12. Consequently, the overall risk coefficient derived by the BEIR IV Committee (ie an excess relative risk of 2.5×10^{-2} WLM^{-1} at ages 55–64 years following exposure 5–14 years earlier) is weighted by the data for these two mines and differs by not more than a factor of about two from the risk coefficients for the individual mines considered by BEIR IV.

	Average exposure rate (WLM y^{-1})	Excess relative risk (10^{-2} WLM^{-1})	
Mine(s)		Original (95% confidence interval)	BEIR IV[a]
Colorado Plateau, USA	124	1.2	0.9[b]
Port Radium, Canada	109	0.27 (0.11–0.43)	—
Newfoundland, Canada	67	0.9 (0.6–1.2)	—
Yunnan Province, China	20	0.6 (0.4–0.8)	—
New Mexico, USA	16 (approx)	1.1	
Ontario, Canada	10 (approx)	1.3	1.8
Cornwall, UK	10 (approx)	0.9 (0.5–1.4)	—
Malmberget, Sweden	5	3.6 (2.2–5.0)	3.6
Beaverlodge, Canada	5	3.3 (2.1–4.5)	5.1

TABLE 4.12 Relative risk coefficients in relation to exposure rate in mines (after Darby and Doll[65])

Notes
(a) Based on those aged 55–64 years with exposure 5–14 years previously.
(b) Based on cumulative exposures of less than 2000 WLM.

89   Within studies at a given mine, there was evidence of an increase in the risk per cumulative exposure with decreasing exposure rate in the Colorado Plateau study, after excluding the data on the highest cumulative exposures for which uncertainty exists in the exposure estimates. The BEIR IV Committee also noted a suggestion of such an effect within the Beaverlodge study but, because it was not apparent within the other cohorts that were examined (Ontario and Malmberget), it was not included in the final

risk model. However, an exposure rate effect of the above form has now been reported for the Czech and Chinese studies, although the reports of other studies either have not addressed this question or have been unable to provide any information owing to the lack of variation in exposure rates within certain mines (for example, as in Cornwall). There are some indications of an inverse exposure rate effect from some studies in rats[72,73], although this may have been chiefly the result of cell killing at high doses[74,75].

90   To conclude, there is some indication from certain miner studies (in particular, that at Port Radium) of lower risk coefficients at higher exposure rates. Obviously, however, any exposure rate effect would disappear at sufficiently low exposure rates. It should also be emphasised that the BEIR IV analysis took account of the two cohorts with the highest reported risk coefficients and so the BEIR IV risk coefficient differs from the highest value in an individual study by only about a factor of two. As with the topics discussed above, it may ultimately be possible to examine any exposure rate effect using information from the studies of indoor radon exposure.

Epidemiological studies of lung cancer and indoor radon exposure

91   Whilst a number of correlation studies of lung cancer and mean radon concentrations have been carried out in various countries, these have been unsatisfactory, owing to the general lack of information on smoking in these studies and the fact that they tend to be based on large geographical areas. Consequently the emphasis is now on studies that collect data on individual radon exposures, as well as smoking habits and other possible confounders. In particular, about 15 case–control studies are currently being performed throughout the world, mainly in Europe (including southwest England) and North America. With the need to collect detailed data, such studies can be time-consuming to undertake. There is also the problem of attempting to estimate exposures that were received many years previously, possibly in one or more previous dwellings. The effect of random errors in the assessment of indoor radon exposure would be to obscure the relationship with the risk of lung cancer. It is therefore planned to pool the results of the individual studies when these are completed, so as to increase the statistical power of the test for trend in the lung cancer risk with radon exposure.

92   At present very few of these studies have reported results. There have been indications from studies in Sweden[76-78] of an increase in lung cancer risk in relation to indirect estimates of radon exposures, based on house type and geology. In a later study of 210 women in Stockholm county with lung cancer and 410 controls for which radon measurements were made in dwellings, Pershagen *et al*[79] showed an increasing trend in risk with cumulative radon exposure; for exposure in excess of 5000 Bq m^{-3} y compared with less than 1250 Bq m^{-3} y, the relative risk was 2.3 (95% confidence interval 1.1–4.5). The excess relative risk per unit exposure estimated from this study, namely 2.7 10^{-2} WLM^{-1}, is within the range of values arising from studies of miners, as shown in Table 4.12. Schoenberg *et al*[80] conducted a study in New Jersey (USA) in which year-long alpha track detector measurements were made in dwellings that had been occupied for at least ten years by 433 female lung cancer cases and 402 controls. The study yielded an excess relative risk of 3.4 10^{-2} WLM^{-1} (90% confidence interval 0.0–8.0 10^{-2} WLM^{-1}) which is within the range cited in Table 4.12 for the miner studies. The authors did caution that less than 50% of the potential subjects were included in this study, owing in part to the exclusion of the more mobile section of the population

who did not meet the above residence criterion. A study in China[81] of about 300 female lung cancer cases and a similar number of controls failed to show a correlation with indoor radon; radon data were available for a smaller proportion of the eligible cases (74%) than for the controls (90%), although the population was less mobile than in other studies. In Finland, a study of 238 male lung cancer cases and 434 controls (mostly smokers in both groups) indicated an increasing risk with increasing radon exposure which, whilst not statistically significant, was consistent with the BEIR IV and ICRP risk estimates[82]. However, the controls tended to differ from the cases in terms of vital status, and measured radon levels were obtained for only 72% of the cases and 79% of the controls.

93   As stated earlier, it will be necessary to wait until results from further studies are published and then pooled before it will be possible to obtain an overall idea of the magnitude of the risks associated with indoor exposure. In doing so, it will be important to adjust for the effect of random errors in the exposure estimates.

Radon and cancers other than lung

94   Some of the studies of miners, such as those in Ontario, Malmberget (Sweden) and Cornwall, have shown raised risks of stomach cancer relative to national levels. However, in Ontario, stomach cancer rates were raised to a similar extent among a group of gold miners, who received much lower radon exposures than the uranium miners. Questions have been raised as to whether exposure to dust or physical exertion plays a role in the aetiology of this cancer, although in the Cornish study there was no association between the stomach cancer risk and the time spent working underground. The study of Cornwall tin miners[69] also reported an excess of leukaemia, although based on small numbers (7 observed, 4.1 expected). Apart from an insignificant excess of lymphoma in the Swedish study (7 observed, 4.7 expected), other studies of miners have not reported such an excess, and the authors of the Cornish study found it difficult to see that radon could have affected the risk of leukaemia. An overview of risks of cancer other than in the miner cohorts is currently being conducted, under the coordination of the Imperial Cancer Research Fund, Oxford.

95   Henshaw *et al*[83] claimed that indoor radon exposure is associated with the risk of leukaemia and certain other cancers, such as melanoma and cancers of the kidney and prostate. These claims were based in large part on an international correlation study, in which national cancer incidence rates and mean indoor radon concentrations in different countries were compared. However, as Butland *et al*[84] pointed out, it is very difficult to place any interpretation on these results, owing to the wide variation in the quality of the radon data between countries, as well as some variation in the quality of the cancer data. In particular, Nordic countries, where cancer registries have been operating for a long period and the quality of the cancer data is high, tend to have the highest national radon levels. It is also difficult to interpret results presented by Henshaw *et al* within certain countries (eg Canada) since they still relate to large geographical areas.

96   An analysis has recently been performed by the Board and the Childhood Cancer Research Group (University of Oxford) of childhood leukaemia and non-Hodgkin's lymphoma in small areas (namely, districts) throughout Britain in relation to indoor radon concentrations and indoor and outdoor gamma dose rates[85]. Taken over all

districts, there were no significant correlations between childhood leukaemia incidence and the levels of natural radiation. When the data were amalgamated into larger areas, namely counties, there were indications of a positive trend in leukaemia incidence with indoor radon level and of a negative trend with indoor gamma dose rate. However, when the district-level data adjusted for county were studied, these trends were reversed although they were not statistically significant. The differences between the results from the analyses based, respectively, on county-level data and on district-level data adjusted for county did not seem to be explainable on the basis of uncertainties in the estimates of natural radiation levels. Rather, Muirhead *et al*[85] concluded that geographical confounding factors are likely to have affected the former analysis (which was based on larger areas) and that, after allowing for county effects, the data do not support the claims of Henshaw *et al*[83].

97   The results obtained by Muirhead *et al*[85] reinforce the view that correlation studies based on large areas are often likely to be misleading because of confounding factors, and that it is better to look at data pertaining to small areas (as did Muirhead *et al*) or to individuals, as in a cohort or a case–control study. The cohort approach is being followed by the Imperial Cancer Research Fund, the Board and the London School of Hygiene and Tropical Medicine, which are currently collaborating in a study of mortality and cancer incidence. This cohort consists of people who, in the past, lived in certain dwellings in Devon and Cornwall where radon measurements have been made. The case–control approach is being taken for a study in the USA by the National Cancer Institute and the Children's Cancer Group. This study involves about 600 newly-diagnosed cases of childhood acute lymphoblastic leukaemia and 600 matched controls, for whom measurements of radon levels will be made in their dwellings[86]. A similar study of childhood cancer has commenced in Britain, under the direction of the UK Coordinating Committee on Cancer Research. These studies should have reasonably high statistical power to detect any associations, whilst avoiding the problems inherent in comparing data across large geographical areas.

CONCLUSIONS

98   Based on the epidemiological studies summarised in paragraphs 1–11 and on the models described in paragraphs 57–75, the lifetime risk of fatal radiation-induced cancer in a UK population of all ages and both sexes has been estimated as $5.9 \ 10^{-2} \ Sv^{-1}$ for exposure to low doses or at low dose rates from low LET radiation. The corresponding value for a UK working population exposed at ages 18–64 years is $5.0 \ 10^{-2} \ Sv^{-1}$. These values are higher than those given by Stather *et al*[13] owing mainly to the use of a DDREF of 2 for all organs, rather than 3. They are also slightly higher than those of ICRP[15] owing mainly to higher baseline cancer rates in the UK compared with a world average. However, there are still uncertainties in these risk estimates, related mainly to the form of the risk models. In particular, the risk up to 40 years following exposure is estimated as $2.4 \ 10^{-2} \ Sv^{-1}$ for the general population and $3.0 \ 10^{-2} \ Sv^{-1}$ for a working population. Consequently if the relative risk of most solid cancers were not to remain constant over a lifetime (as assumed in the above calculation of lifetime risks for solid cancers other than lung) but to decrease beyond the current period of follow-up for the

Japanese atomic bomb survivors, then the risks could turn out to be lower than those predicted under a relative risk projection model. This uncertainty is greatest for those irradiated early in life.

99   It should be possible to reduce some of the uncertainties in risk estimates as follows.

(i)   For the projection of risks over time, continued follow-up of irradiated groups such as the Japanese atomic bomb survivors will be of special importance. This is particularly true for those irradiated early in life who are now reaching the ages at which baseline cancer rates increase substantially. Further parallel analyses would be of help in combining information from different studies on the temporal pattern seen within the current period of follow-up.

(ii)   In deciding how to transfer across populations, parallel analyses of studies from different countries, such as of breast cancer in Japan and North America, are very important and should be encouraged.

(iii)   More information on the risks associated with low dose/low dose rate exposures may be obtained from epidemiological studies based on such exposures, eg of those exposed occupationally. Although the studies performed to date lack sufficient statistical power to determine risks with any great precision, precision may be increased with the initiation of further worker studies and the pooled analysis of these studies under the coordination of the International Agency for Research on Cancer.

100   At the current time, however, there is the possibility that the total cancer risk for the general population could be up to a factor of about 2 less than the value based on the lifetime projection, owing to uncertainty concerning the future pattern of risks. Independently of that factor, uncertainty concerning the choice of DDREF could mean that the risk is too high or too low by a factor of possibly 2. For individual cancer types, there is additionally an uncertainty of a factor of 2 or more associated with the method of transferring risks across populations and with statistical uncertainties in the source data. However, for leukaemia, the uncertainty associated with the projection of risks across time and populations and with statistical uncertainties in the source data is probably only about a factor of 1.5 in total, whilst the uncertainty in DDREF is about a factor of 2, based on a dose–response analysis for the Japanese atomic bomb survivors.

101   In its assessment of uncertainties, the BEIR V Committee[3] concentrated on quantifying the statistical uncertainties in the source data, but recognised that uncertainties of other types may exist. One type concerns the specification of the form of the risk model; as pointed out above, this is likely to represent a major component of uncertainty in risk estimates. Another type of uncertainty relates to the quality of the source data. Of particular relevance here is the reliability of disease classification and of dose estimates for groups studied epidemiologically. For example, Sposto *et al*[87] concluded on the basis of data for acute radiation effects that there may be random errors of 45%–50% in the DS86 dosimetry for the Japanese atomic bomb survivors; the possibility of systematic errors in DS86 is more problematic[88,89]. To combine all these different types of uncertainty would not be straightforward, given that not all of them can be quantified.

102   The lifetime risk of fatal lung cancer in a general UK population exposed to indoor radon has been estimated as 3.5×10^{-4} WLM^{-1}. This arises from applying the relative risk

model of ICRP[57] to UK baseline lung cancer rates, and is also the same as the estimate of the BEIR IV Committee[2]. This estimate, which is also used for workers, is based on studies of miners exposed occupationally to radon, and there are some uncertainties concerning the use of these data to estimate risks for a general population exposed in an indoor environment. Some of these uncertainties may be reduced by further analyses of the miner data; for example, by studying the interaction between radon and smoking and the possibility of an exposure rate effect. However, in order to examine other uncertainties, such as risks to females and of exposure early in life, the best means may be the many case–control studies of indoor radon exposure and lung cancer that are currently being performed, mainly in Europe and North America. Statistical power considerations suggest that it will be necessary to wait until these studies are published and then pooled before results of reasonable precision are obtained. Whilst a correlation study based on small area data from throughout Britain has not shown any statistically significant correlation between indoor radon and childhood leukaemia[85], cohort and case–control studies are currently being conducted to look for any association between radon and cancers other than lung.

103   A future goal in quantifying radiation-induced risks would be the use of models developed from mechanisms of tumorigenesis. Although some illustrative calculations have been performed here, current knowledge of mechanisms is not sufficient to allow such models to replace the empirical models used to derive the above risk estimates. However, further investigation of mechanisms may well be of importance in determining the form of risk models.

REFERENCES

1   UNSCEAR. Sources, effects and risks of ionising radiation. 1988 report to the General Assembly, with annexes. New York, United Nations (1988).

2   BEIR IV. Health risks of radon and other internally deposited alpha-emitters. Washington DC, NAS/NRC (1988).

3   BEIR V. Health effects of exposure to low levels of ionising radiation. Washington DC, NAS/NRC (1990).

4   Shimizu, Y, Kato, H, and Schull, W J. Life Span Study Report 11, Part II: Cancer mortality in the years 1950–1985 based on the recently revised doses (DS86). Hiroshima, Radiation Effects Research Foundation, Report TR5-88 (1988).

5   Darby, S C, Doll, R, Gill, S K, and Smith, P G. Long-term mortality after a single treatment course with x-rays in patients treated for ankylosing spondylitis. *Br. J. Cancer,* **55**, 179–90 (1987).

6   Miller, A B, Howe, G R, Sherman, G J, Lindsay, J P, Yaffe, M J, Dinner, P J, Risch, H A, and Preston, D L. Mortality from breast cancer after irradiation during fluoroscopic examinations in patients being treated for tuberculosis. *N. Engl J. Med.,* **321**, 1285–9 (1989).

7   Ron, E, Modan, B, and Boice J D. Mortality after radiotherapy for ringworm of the scalp. *Am. J. Epidemiol.,* **127**, 713–24 (1988).

8   Ron, E, Modan, B, Preston, D L, Alfandary, E, Stovall, M, and Boice J D. Thyroid neoplasia following low-dose radiation in childhood. *Radiat. Res.,* **120**, 516–31 (1989).

9   Ron, E, Modan, B, Preston, D L, Alfandary, E, Stovall, M, and Boice J D. Radiation-induced skin carcinomas of the head and neck. *Radiat. Res.,* **125**, 318–25 (1991).

10   Kendall, G M, Muirhead, C R, MacGibbon, B H, O'Hagan, J A, Conquest, A J, Goodill, A A, Butland, B K, Fell, T P, Jackson, D A, Webb, M A, Haylock, R G E, Thomas, J M, and Silk, T J. Mortality and occupational exposure to radiation: First analysis of the National Registry for Radiation Workers. *Br. Med. J.,* **304**, 220–5 (1992).

11   Roesch, W J (ed). Final report of the US–Japan reassessment of atomic bomb radiation dosimetry in Hiroshima and Nagasaki. Hiroshima, Radiation Effects Research Foundation (1987).

12 BEIR III. The effects on populations of exposure to low levels of ionising radiation. Washington DC, NAS/NRC (1980).

13 Stather, J W, Muirhead, C R, Edwards, A A, Harrison, J D, Lloyd, D C, and Wood, N R. Health effects models developed from the 1988 UNSCEAR report. Chilton, NRPB-R226 (London, HMSO) (1988).

14 Shimizu, Y, Kato, H, Schull, W J, and Hoel, D G. Studies of the mortality of A-bomb survivors. 9. Mortality, 1950–1985: Part 3. Non-cancer mortality based on the revised doses (DS86). *Radiat. Res.*, **130**, 249 (1992).

15 ICRP. 1990 Recommendations of the International Commission on Radiological Protection. ICRP Publication 60. *Ann. ICRP*, **21**, Nos 1–3 (1991).

16 Armitage, P, and Doll, R. The age distribution of cancer and a multi-stage theory of carcinogenesis. *Br. J. Cancer*, **8**, 1–12 (1954).

17 Thomas, D C. Temporal effects and interactions in cancer: Implications of carcinogenic models. IN Environmental Epidemiology: Risk Assessment (Eds R L Prentice and A S Whittemore). Philadelphia, SIAM 107–21 (1982).

18 Moolgavkar, S H, and Knudson A G. Mutation and cancer: A model for human carcinogenesis. *J. Natl Cancer Inst.*, **66**, 1037–52 (1981).

19 Doll, R, and Peto, R. The causes of cancer: Quantitative estimates of avoidable risks of cancer in the United States today. *J. Natl Cancer Inst.*, **66**, 1193 (1981).

20 Pearce, N. Multistage modelling of lung cancer mortality in asbestos textile workers. *Int. J. Epidemiol.*, **17**, 747–52 (1988).

21 Day, N E. Radiation and multistage carcinogenesis. IN *Radiation Carcinogenesis: Epidemiology and Biological Significance* (Eds J D Boice and J F Fraumeni). New York, Raven Press, pp 437–43 (1984).

22 Moolgavkar, S H, Cross, F T, Luebeck, G, and Dagle, G E. A two-mutation model for radon-induced lung tumours in rats. *Radiat. Res.*, **121**, 28–37 (1990).

23 Thomas, D C. A model for dose rate and duration of exposure effects in radiation carcinogenesis. *Environ. Health Perspect.*, **87**, 163–71 (1990).

24 Little, M P, Hawkins, M M, Shore, R E, Charles, M W, and Hildreth, N G. Time variations in the risk of cancer following irradiation in childhood. *Radiat. Res.*, **126**, 304–16 (1991).

25 Boice, J D, Day, N E, Andersen, A, *et al.* Second cancers following radiation treatment for cervical cancer. An international collaboration among cancer registries. *J. Natl Cancer Inst.*, **74**, 955–75 (1985).

26 Muirhead, C R, and Darby, S C. Relative and absolute risk models for cancer mortality in ankylosing spondylitis patients. IN *Low Dose Radiation: Biological Bases of Risk Assessment* (Eds K F Baverstock and J W Stather). London, Taylor and Francis, pp 162–70 (1989).

27 Tokunaga, M, Land, C E, Yamamoto, T, Asano, M, Tokuoka, S, Ezaki, H, and Nishimori, I. Incidence of female breast cancer among atomic bomb survivors, Hiroshima and Nagasaki, 1950–1980. *Radiat. Res.*, **112**, 243–72 (1987).

28 Shore, R E, Hildreth, N, Woodard, E D, Dvoretsky, P, Hempleman, L, and Pasternack, B S. Breast cancer among women given x-ray therapy for acute postpartum mastitis. *J. Natl Cancer Inst.*, **77**, 689–96 (1986).

29 Boice, J D, Preston, D L, Davis, F G, and Monson, R R. Frequent chest x-ray fluoroscopy and breast cancer incidence among tuberculosis patients in Massachusetts. *Radiat. Res.*, **125**, 214–22 (1991).

30 Preston, D L. Presentation at the USDOE/RERF/IARC/CEC workshop on 'The Future of Human Radiation Research', Schloss Elmau, Germany, March 1991.

31 Shore, R E, Woodard, E, Hildreth, N, Dvoretsky, P, Hempleman, L, and Pasternack, B S. Thyroid tumours following thymus irradiation. *J. Natl Cancer Inst.*, **74**, 1177–84 (1985).

32 Shore, R E, Albert R E, Reed, M, Harley, N, and Pasternack, B S. Skin cancer incidence among children irradiated for ringworm of the scalp. *Radiat. Res.*, **100**, 192–204 (1984).

33 Muir, C, Waterhouse, J, Mack, T, Powell, J, and Whelan, S (eds). *Cancer Incidence in Five Continents, Volume V.* Lyon, International Agency for Research on Cancer (1987).

34 Land, C E, and Sinclair, W K. The relative contributions of different organ sites to the total cancer mortality associated with low-dose radiation exposure. *Ann. ICRP*, **22**, No. 1, 31–57 (1991).

35 Land, C E, Boice, J D, Shore, R E, Norman, J E, and Tokunaga, M. Breast cancer risk from low-dose exposures to ionising radiation: Results of parallel analysis of three exposed populations of women. *J. Natl Cancer Inst.*, **65**, 353–65 (1980).

36 Land, C E. Radiation dose, reproductive history, and breast cancer risk among Japanese A-bomb survivors: Preliminary findings. *Radiat. Res.*, **131**, 119 (1993).

37 Lewis, C A, Smith, P G, Stratton, I M, Darby, S C, and Doll, R. Estimated radiation doses to different organs among patients treated for ankylosing spondylitis with a single course of x-rays. *Br. J. Radiol.*, **61**, 212–20 (1988).

38 Kopecky, K J, Nakashima, E, Yamamoto, T, and Kato, H. Lung cancer, radiation and smoking among A-bomb survivors, Hiroshima and Nagasaki. Hiroshima, Radiation Effects Research Foundation, Report TR13-86 (1986).

39 Sevc, J, Kunz, E, Tomasek, L, Placek, V, and Heracek, J. Cancer in man after exposure to radon daughters. *Health Phys.*, **54**, 27–46 (1989).

40 Shore, R E. The epidemiology of radiation-induced thyroid cancer: research issues and needs. IN *The Future of Human Radiation Research* (Eds G B Gerber *et al*). London, British Institute of Radiology, Report 22, pp 61–6 (1991).

41 Storer, J B, Mitchell, T J, and Fry, R J M. Extrapolation of the relative risk of radiogenic neoplasms across mouse strains to man. *Radiat. Res.*, **114**, 331–53 (1988).

42 Little, M P, and Charles, M W. Time variations in radiation-induced relative risk and implications for population cancer risks. *J. Radiol. Prot.*, **11**, 91–110 (1991).

43 Muirhead, C R. Projection of radiation-induced cancer risks across time and populations. *Radiat. Prot. Dosim.*, **36**, 321–5 (1991).

44 Pierce, D A, and Vaeth, M. The shape of the cancer mortality dose-response curve for atomic bomb survivors. *Radiat. Res.*, **126**, 36–42 (1991).

45 Boice, J D, Blettner, M, Kleinerman, R A, *et al*. Radiation dose and leukaemia risk in patients treated for cancer of the cervix. *J. Natl Cancer Inst.*, **79**, 1295–311 (1987).

46 Gilbert, E S, Fry, S A, Wiggs, L D, Voelz, G L, Cragle, D L, and Petersen, G R. Analyses of combined mortality data on workers at the Hanford site, Oak Ridge National Laboratory and Rocky Flats nuclear weapons plant. *Radiat. Res.*, **120**, 19–35 (1989).

47 Robb, J D. Estimates of radiation detriment in a UK population. Chilton, NRPB (to be published).

48 OPCS. Historic mortality data files – update for 1984 and 1985. London, OPCS (supplied on magnetic tape) (1987).

49 Hoel, D G. Personal Communication (1990).

50 Gilbert, E S. Late somatic effects. IN Health Effects Model for Nuclear Power Plant Accident Consequence Analysis. Part II. Scientific Basis for Health Effects Models. Washington DC, US Nuclear Regulatory Commission, NUREG/CR-4214 (SAND 85-7185) (1985).

51 National Council on Radiation Protection and Measurements. Induction of thyroid cancer by ionising radiation. Bethesda, MD, NCRP, Report No. 80 (1985).

52 OPCS. Cancer statistics: Incidence, survival and mortality in England and Wales. Studies on medical and population subjects, No. 43. London, HMSO (1981).

53 ICRP. Quantitative bases for developing a unified index of harm. ICRP Publication 45. *Ann. ICRP*, **4**, Nos 1–2 (1985).

54 NRPB. Human exposure to radon in homes: Recommendation for the practical application of the Board's statement. *Doc. NRPB*, **1**, 17 (1990).

55 Radford, E P, and St Clair Renard, K G. Lung cancer in swedish iron ore miners exposed to low doses of radon daughters. *New Engl. J. Med.*, **310**, 1485–94 (1984).

56 Muller, J, Wheeler, W C, Gentleman, J F, Suranyi, G, and Kusiak, R. Study of mortality of Ontario miners. Presented at International Conference on Occupational Radiation Safety in Mining, October 1984, Toronto, Canada (1984).

57 ICRP. Lung cancer risk from indoor exposures to radon daughters. ICRP Publication 50. *Ann. ICRP*, **17**, No. 1 (1987).

58 NAS/NRC. Comparative dosimetry of radon in mines and homes. Washington DC, National Academy Press (1991).

59 Xuan, X Z, Lubin, J H, Li, J Y, Yang, L F, Luo, Q S, Yang, L, Wang, J Z, and Blot, W J. A cohort study in Southern China of tin miners exposed to radon and radon decay products. *Health Phys.*, **64**, 120 (1993).

60   Roscoe, R J, Steenland, K, Halperin, W E, Beaumont, J J, and Waxweiler, R J. Lung cancer mortality among non-smoking uranium miners exposed to radon daughters. *JAMA.*, **262**, 629–33 (1989).

61   Samet, J M, Pathak, D R, Morgan, M V, Key, C R, Valdevia, A A, and Lubin, J H. Lung cancer mortality and exposure to radon progeny in a cohort of New Mexico underground uranium miners. *Health Phys.*, **61**, 745 (1991).

62   L'Abbé, K A, Howe, G R, Burch, J D, Miller, A B, Abbatt, J, Band, P, Choi, W, Du, J, Feather, J, Gallagher, R, Hill, G, and Matthews, V. Radon exposure, cigarette smoking, and other mining experience in the Beaverlodge uranium miners cohort. *Health Phys.*, **60**, 489–95 (1991).

63   Morrison, H I, Semenciw, R M, Mao, Y, and Wigle, D T. Cancer mortality among a group of fluorspar miners exposed to radon progency. *Am. J. Epidemiol.*, **128**, 1266–75 (1988).

64   Darby, S C, and Doll, R. Radiation and exposure rate. *Nature*, **344**, 824 (1990).

65   Darby, S C, and Doll, R. Radon in houses: How large is the risk? *Radiat. Prot. Aus.*, **8**, 83–8 (1991).

66   Hornung, R W, and Meinhardt, T J. Quantitative risk assessment of lung cancer in US uranium miners. *Health Phys.*, **52**, 417 (1987).

67   Howe, G R, Nair, R C, Newcombe, H B, Miller, A B, and Abbatt, J D. Lung cancer mortality (1950–80) in relation to radon daughter exposure in a cohort of workers at the Eldorado Beaverlodge uranium mine. *J. Natl Cancer Inst.*, **77**, 357 (1986).

68   Howe, G R, Nair, R C, Newcombe, H B, Miller, A B, Burch, J D, and Abbatt, J D. Lung cancer mortality (1950–80) in relation to radon daughter exposure in a cohort of workers at the Eldorado Port Radium uranium mine: Possible modification of risk by exposure rate. *J. Natl Cancer Inst.*, **79**, 1255 (1987).

69   Hodgson, J T, and Jones, R D. Mortality of a cohort of tin miners, 1941–86. *Br. J. Indust. Med.*, **47**, 665–76 (1990).

70   Woodward, A, Roder, D, McMichael, A J, Crouch, P, and Mylvaganam, A. Radon daughter exposures at the Radium Hill uranium mine and lung cancer rates among former workers, 1952–87. *Cancer Causes Control*, **2**, 213 (1991).

71   Howe, G R. Personal Communication (1992).

72   Gilbert, E S. Lung cancer risk models from experimental animals. IN *Proceedings 24th Annual Meeting of the National Council on Radiation Protection and Measurements*. Bethesda, MD, NCRP, Proceedings No. 10 (1989).

73   Cross, F T. Experimental studies on lung carcinogenesis and their relationship to future research on radiation-induced lung cancer in humans. IN *The Future of Human Radiation Research* (Eds G B Gerber *et al*). London, British Institute of Radiology, Report 22, pp 27–35 (1991).

74   Gray, R G, Lafuma, J, and Paris, S E. Lung tumours and radon inhalation in over 2000 rats: Approximate linearity across a wide range of doses and potentiation by tobacco smoke. IN: *Lifespan Radiation Effects Studies in Animals: What Can They Tell Us?* (Eds R C Thompson and J A Mahaffey). Springfield, VA, NTIS, pp 592–607 (1986).

75   Morlier, J P, Morin, M, Chameaud, J, *et al*. Importance du rôle du débit de dose sur l'apparition des cancers chez le rat après inhalation de radon. *C. R. Acad. Sci. Paris*, **t. 315**, Serie III, 436–66 (1992).

76   Edling, C, Kling, H, and Axelson, O. Radon in homes – a possible cause of lung cancer. *Scand. J. Work Environ. Health.*, **10**, 25–34 (1984).

77   Svensson, C, Eklund, G, and Pershagen, G. Indoor exposure to radon from the ground and bronchial cancer in women. *Int. Arch. Occup. Environ. Health*, **59**, 123–31 (1987).

78   Svensson, C, Pershagen, G, and Klominck, J. Lung cancer in women and type of dwelling in relation to radon exposure. *Cancer Res.*, **49**, 1861–5 (1989).

79   Pershagen, G, Liang, Z-H, Hrubec, Z, Svensson, C, and Boice, J D. Residential radon exposure and lung cancer in Swedish women. *Health Phys.*, **63**, 179–86 (1992).

80   Schoenberg, J B, Klotz, J B, Wilcox, H B, Nicholls, G P, Gildel-Real, M J, Sternhagen, A, and Mason, T J. Case-control study of residential radon and lung cancer among New Jersey women. *Cancer Res.*, **50**, 6520–24 (1990).

81   Blot, W J, Xu, Z-Y, Boice, J D, Zhao, D-Z, Stone, B J, Sun, J, Jing, L-B, and Fraumeni, J F. Indoor radon and lung cancer in China. *J. Natl Cancer Inst.*, **82**, 1025–30 (1990).

82   Ruosteenoja, E. Indoor radon and risk of lung cancer: An epidemiological study in Finland. Helsinki, Finnish Centre for Radiation and Nuclear Safety, STUK-A99 (1991).

83 Henshaw, D L, Eatough, J P, and Richardson, R B. Radon as a causative factor in induction of myeloid leukaemia and other cancers. *Lancet*, **355**, 1008–12 (1990).

84 Butland, B K, Muirhead, C R, and Draper, G J. Letter to the editor: Radon and leukaemia. *Lancet*, **335**, 1338–9 (1990).

85 Muirhead, C R, Butland, B K, Green, B M R, and Draper, G J. Childhood leukaemia and natural radiation. *Lancet*, **337**, 503-4 (1991).

86 Linet, M S. Personal Communication (1992).

87 Sposto, R, Stram, D O, and Awa, A A. Estimating the magnitude of random errors in the DS86 dosimetry using data on chromosome aberrations and severe epilation. Hiroshima, Radiation Effects Research Foundation, Report TR7-90 (1991).

88 Jablon, S. Neutrons in Hiroshima and uncertainties in cancer risk estimates. *Radiat. Res.*, **133**, 130 (1993).

89 Straume, T, Egbert, S D, Woolson, W A, Finkel, R C, Kubik, P W, Gove, H E, Sharma, P, and Hoshi, M. Neutron discrepancies in the DS86 Hiroshima dosimetry system. *Health Phys.*, **63**, 421 (1992).

90 Thomas, D C, Darby, S, Fagnani, F, Hubert, P, Vaeth, M, and Weiss, K. Definition and estimation of lifetime detriment from radiation exposures: Principles and methods. *Health Phys.*, **63**, 259 (1992).

5 Radiation-induced Hereditary Disease

INTRODUCTION

1   In addition to inducing neoplastic changes in somatic tissues, ionising radiation may also produce transmissible (heritable) effects in an irradiated population through the induction of mutations in the DNA of male and female germ cells. These mutations, whilst having no direct consequences for the exposed individual, may be expressed in subsequent generations as genetic disorders of widely differing types and severity.

CLASSIFICATION AND EXPRESSION OF GENETIC DAMAGE

2   Chromosomal DNA is the repository of the cellular information required for the development and maintenance of all organisms. This information is passed from one generation to the next via the male and female gametes. During the fertilisation process these fuse to form a zygote which, following development, forms the next generation of offspring. The process of gamete formation (gametogenesis), whilst a highly controlled process, is subject to a variety of sources of spontaneous mutation that generate a background level of genetic disorders in all human and animal populations.

3   This spontaneously arising genetic damage in gametes may originate from:

(i)   errors in the replication of DNA,

(ii) misrepair of DNA damage induced by endogenous metabolic processes (these may take the form of changes to the DNA base sequence of single genes or deletion, rearrangement or duplication of larger stretches of DNA encoding perhaps a number of genes),

(iii) numerical changes in the chromosomes of the gametes resulting in aneuploidy.

In general, all these forms of mutation may also be induced by DNA damaging agents present in the environment, including radiation. Such exposures may therefore be expected to increase the frequency of genetically determined disease in the human population.

Gene mutations

4   Three categories of gene mutation may be distinguished, ie dominant, recessive and X-linked. Man is characterised by the possession of 46 chromosomes; 44 of these are present in morphologically identical pairs (the autosomes) and the other two (the X and Y) are sex determining chromosomes with females carrying two copies of X and males carrying single copies of X and Y. The Y chromosome is virtually inert apart from the expression of factors determining maleness. At fertilisation each normal offspring receives, via the gametes, a single set of autosomes from each parent plus one copy of X from the mother and X or Y from the father. If either parent carries a dominant mutation in an autosomally located gene associated with a given disorder then inheritance of this mutant gene will, in general, lead to the expression of that disorder even if its normal counterpart is inherited from the other. In contrast, if the mutant gene

is recessive in its expression then its effect will not be seen unless both copies in the offspring are defective, ie the mutation is present in a homozygous form. Thus, in general, recessive mutations when they first arise do not manifest themselves because the normal gene copy has the capacity to 'shield' its mutated partner; carriers of such mutations are termed heterozygotes and the mutation will not be expressed in offspring unless a mutant gene is also transmitted by the other parent. This could obviously occur if both parents were heterozygotes or if one or, much less frequently, both gametes had sustained a new mutation in the same gene. It is, however, becoming increasingly recognised that in some genetic disorders the distinction between recessive and dominant characteristics is not absolute. Dominant genes may be subject to 'penetrance' effects that can modify the degree of clinical expression and partial clinical effects are not infrequently seen in heterozygotes for some apparently autosomal recessive disorders (see also paragraph 9).

5   In males, where only one copy of the X chromosome is present, all recessive mutations on the X chromosome are expressed. In contrast, since females carry two X chromosome copies that same mutation will not usually be apparent unless both gene copies are defective.

6   The above characteristics imply that, in general, dominantly acting and many X-linked mutations will be expressed in the first generation offspring following germ cell mutation of parents and will then reoccur in subsequent generations provided that they do not have any drastic detrimental effects on reproductive capacity. It also follows that induced autosomal recessive mutations may remain 'dormant' for many generations, the duration of persistence determined by their effects in heterozygotes and their appearance depending on the frequency of heterozygotes and/or the probability of further *de novo* mutational events within the population.

7   Dominant and homozygous recessive mutations may be further subdivided into those that express as disease states in the live-born (visibles) and those that induce prenatal death (lethals). These factors affect both the relative maintenance of such mutations in the population and also their impact on society.

Chromosomal mutations

8   Mutations resulting in gross structural or numerical changes to chromosomes generally produce profound detrimental effects during development of offspring. In many cases these result in complete developmental failure and prenatal death. In the minority of cases where embryonic and fetal development is not terminated the offspring usually exhibit severe physical abnormalities usually accompanied by mental retardation (eg Down's syndrome), which greatly reduce reproductive fitness. Thus, in general, these mutations are not retained in the population and their frequency is maintained largely by *de novo* mutation.

Multifactorial disease

9   Overall, the characteristics of dominant, recessive, X-linked and chromosomally determined genetic disorders are relatively well defined. Although their expression and thereby their apparent frequency in the population may in some cases be subject to other factors (eg variable penetrance and partial effects in heterozygotes), they do permit quantification in both human epidemiological and animal experimental studies. Such definition and quantification is, however, lacking for a broad category of human

disorders termed multifactorial disease. These include many congenital abnormalities and a variety of commonly occurring chronic diseases, many of which are of adult and late-life onset. These have variable genetic components which, in terms of expression, are usually subject to substantial modification by environmental factors. In principle, changes in mutation rates within the population through, for example, radiation exposure, might be expected to increase the frequency of these diseases but, as is discussed later, predictions on radiation-induced genetic risk are highly uncertain.

10   Examples of some hereditary diseases are given in Table 5.1.

EFFECTS OF RADIATION ON GERM CELLS

11   In spite of intensive studies on the possible genetic consequences of radiation exposure to human populations, no statistically significant excess of heritable effects has so far been observed in the limited data available[1,2,3]. The principal source of these data has been the children of radiation-exposed survivors of the Japanese atomic bombings in 1945. Using a variety of genetic endpoints as indicators of possible induced mutations (see paragraph 18), Neel and Schull (cited in reference 2) reported on 30 000 children born to parents irradiated in Hiroshima and Nagasaki. The frequency of genetic abnormalities was compared with that observed in 45 000 children born to control parents. In the study group radiation doses to parents were in the range 0.08–2.00 Gy (average about 0.2 Gy), while control parents were those out of the two cities at the time of the bombings. Subsequent follow-up studies of 31 150 children born to parents receiving > 0.01 Gy and 41 066 controls also failed to detect any statistically significant excess of heritable effects in the exposed group, but analyses were performed on these

TABLE 5.1
Examples of hereditary diseases[1]

Dominant disorders	Congenital cataract
	Cystic kidney disease
	Huntingdon's chorea
X-linked diseases	Haemophilia
	Albinism
	Colour blindness
	Heart valve defects
Autosomal recessive diseases	Cretinism
	Disorders of amino acid metabolism
	Aplastic anaemia
	Muscular dystrophy
Multifactorial diseases	Ankylosing spondylitis
	Varicose veins
	Cleft palate
	Diabetes mellitus
	Schizophrenia
	Asthma
Chromosome anomalies	Down's syndrome

data in order to provide an estimate of the lower limit of acute radiation exposure that would be required to double the spontaneous incidence of genetic damage[3]. These analyses are briefly outlined later in this chapter.

Genetic endpoint and sex	Doubling dose (Gy)
Dominant lethal mutations	
Both sexes	0.4–1.0[a]
Recessive lethal mutations	
Both sexes	1.5–3.0[b]
Dominant visible mutations	
Male	
Skeletal	0.75–1.5[a]
Cataract	2.0–4.0[b]
Other	0.8[a]
Female	0.4–1.6[b]
Recessive visible mutations	
Postgonial, female	0.7–6.0[a]
Gonial, male	1.14[a]
Reciprocal translocations	
Male	
Mouse	0.1–0.5[a]
Rhesus	0.2–0.4[b]
Heritable translocations	
Male	0.12–2.5[b]
Female	0.5–1.0[b]
Congenital malformations	
Female, postgonial	0.25–2.5[b]
Male, postgonial	1.25–12.5[b]
Male, gonial	0.8–25.0[b]
Aneuploidy	
Female	
Preovulatory oocyte	0.15–2.5[b]
Less mature oocyte	2.5–13.0[b]
Median (mouse, all endpoints, both sexes)	
Direct estimates	0.7–0.8[a]
Indirect estimates	1.5[b]
Overall	1.0–1.14

TABLE 5.2
Estimated mutational doubling doses for chronic radiation exposure, principally in the mouse[4,6]

Notes
(a) Based on low dose rate irradiation studies.
(b) Based on high dose rate irradiation studies and corrected for dose rate.

12   In the absence of any directly informative positive human data, experimental studies on genetic endpoints in the offspring of irradiated animals (principally mice) have been used to project estimates of radiation-induced heritable effects to exposed human populations[2,4,5]. These genetic endpoints are discussed in the references cited above and also illustrated in Tables 5.2 and 5.3.

TABLE 5.3
Estimated mutational doubling doses for acute irradiation of mouse spermatogonia[6–8]

Mutation system (strain)	Doubling doses (Gy)
Seven locus (101 × C3H)	0.44
Dominant visibles (various)	0.16
Dominant cataract (101/E1 × C3H/E1)	1.57
Skeletal malformation (101)	0.26
Histocompatibility loci (C57BL/6JN)	> 2.60
Recessive lethals (DBA)	0.51
(C3H/HeH × 101/H)	0.80
(CBA, C3H)	4.00
Loci encoding specific proteins	0.11
Recessive visibles	3.89
Average	1.35

PROJECTION OF GENETIC RISKS

13   Two methods have been used for the purpose of projecting experimental animal data to genetic risks in radiation-exposed human populations.

(i)   *Direct method* The direct method, as currently used[9,10], is based on the extrapolation of first generation dominant genetic effects in the mouse, principally those affecting the skeleton and cataracts. The assumption made is that the frequency of induction of these genetic disorders in man is the same, per unit dose, as that in the mouse. Thus, the total of all dominant mutations induced in man by radiation is derived from the ratios of the spontaneous incidence of these specific dominant disorders in man to that for all other dominant disorders. For this purpose McKusick's Catalog[11] is used.

(ii)   *Indirect method* The indirect (or doubling dose) method assumes that mutation rate is linearly proportional to dose and expresses genetic risk relative to the natural incidence of genetic disorders in the population by the equation:

risk = natural prevalence × reciprocal of the doubling dose

The doubling dose is the amount of radiation required to induce as many mutations as those arising spontaneously in a generation. It follows, therefore, that the lower the value of the doubling dose the greater is the relative mutation risk.

14   For populations that are not exposed to irradiation the assumption is made from population genetic theory that there exists an equilibrium between spontaneously arising mutations and those eliminated in each generation by selective processes, principally reproductive fitness. Thus, under conditions of continuous irradiation and a commensurate increase in mutation rate, a new equilibrium position is reached; from this the increased risk to the first generation may then be estimated. For populations exposed to a single acute dose of radiation the mutation frequency is initially increased but this will, through selection over a number of generations, reduce to that of the original equilibrium value. Population genetic theory predicts that the integrated risk over all generations following a single exposure will be the same (per generation) as that produced at equilibrium when the same dose is delivered to each generation.

15   While these arguments can be straightforwardly applied to those genetic disorders where there is a direct relationship between mutation and disease it is increasingly recognised that most 'heritable' diseases have complex aetiology and such simple relationships do not therefore apply. This is particularly important for congenital abnormalities and multifactorial diseases and for these a mutational component needs to be assumed and incorporated into the calculation of genetic risk.

Gene and chromosomal mutations

16   Although both the direct and indirect methods were used in early estimates of genetic risk the BEIR V Committee[4] and ICRP[5], whilst recognising considerable uncertainty, now favour the application of the indirect, doubling dose procedure (see reference 4 for discussion). Table 5.2 shows the range of mutational doubling doses for various genetic endpoints determined for chronic radiation exposure to experimental animals; these are derived from data collated in the BEIR V report[4]. From these, the BEIR V Committee recommended that the average doubling dose for genetic effects is about 1 Gy. Following their own deliberations, the same recommendation is also made by UNSCEAR[2] and ICRP[5]. From Table 5.2 it may be seen, however, that individual doubling doses vary by factors between 2 and 20. These uncertainties are re-enforced by data (Table 5.3) recently collated by Neel and Lewis[8] and further discussed by Neel[7,12] and Sankaranarayanan[6]. These refer to genetic effects following acute high dose irradiation of mouse spermatogonia and, with a dose and dose rate reduction factor of three[1,13] (see also Chapter 3), provide a doubling dose for chronic irradiation of about 4 Gy (range 0.4–12.0 Gy)[6]. Thus on the basis of the two sets of animal data illustrated here it is possible to project a chronic doubling dose for overall genetic effects in the range 1–4 Gy but, clearly, with large and poorly quantifiable uncertainties.

17   Table 5.4 summarises UNSCEAR[1,2,13,14], BEIR[4,15] and ICRP[5] projections for the induction of heritable disease in man on the basis of a doubling dose of about 1 Gy (BEIR[15] used 0.5–2.5 Gy). Thus, in all cases the doubling dose value used appears conservative. To a large extent this caution reflects the current uncertainties regarding genetic risk projection in the absence of any directly informative human data on genetic effects in the Japanese studies. Recently, however, attempts have been made to provide some estimate of genetic risk from these essentially negative findings in humans.

18   The follow-up studies of the Japanese children by Neel *et al*[3] included eight indicators of possible heritable effects in the F1 progeny:

(i)   untoward pregnancy outcome (UPO),
(ii)   mortality (excluding UPO),

(iii)   cancer,

(iv)   balanced chromosomal rearrangement,

(v)   sex chromosome aneuploidy,

(vi)   mutations in selected protein loci,

(vii)   sex ratios,

(viii)   growth and development.

TABLE 5.4a
Probability of severe hereditary effects estimated using the doubling dose method after 1 Gy low dose rate, low LET radiation to the parental population. The doubling dose assumed is 1 Gy (from ICRP[5])

Source	Doubling dose (Gy)	Natural prevalence of genetic disorders (10^{-2})	Radiation-induced probability (10^{-2} Gy^{-1})		
			First generation	Second generation	All generations at equilibrium
UNSCEAR 1977[1]	1	10.51	0.63	–	1.85
UNSCEAR 1982[14]	1	10.63	0.22	–	~1.50
UNSCEAR 1986[13] (excl. multifactorial)	1	1.63	0.18	–	1.04
UNSCEAR 1988[2] (excl. multifactorial and numerical chromosomal)	1	~1.30	~0.18 ⎫ 0.14 ⎬ 0.32 ⎭		~1.20
BEIR 1980[15]	0.5–2.5	10.70	0.15–0.75		0.60–1.10
BEIR 1990[4] (incl. congen. abnorm., excl. common multifactorial.)	1	3.6–4.6	0.15–0.40	–	1.15–2.15

TABLE 5.4b
ICRP current estimates of risk coefficients for serious hereditary effects of ionising radiation (from Sankaranarayanan[16])

Time span	Disease category	Risk coefficients (10^{-2} Gy^{-1})		
		Reproductive population[c]	Total population[c]	Working population[d]
All generations	Mendelian and chromosomal	1.2	0.5	0.3
	Multifactorial[a,b]	1.2	0.5	0.3
	Total	2.4[e,f]	1.0[e]	0.6[e]
First two generations	Mendelian and chromosomal	0.3	0.1	0.07
	Multifactorial	0.23	0.09	0.06
	Total	0.53	0.19	0.13

Notes

(a) Includes congenital abnormalities and common diseases of adults such as those listed in Table 1 of Sankaranarayanan[16].

(b) The risk coefficients for this category have been derived using assumptions outlined in the text and further discussed by Sankaranarayanan[16].

(c) Assumes a reproductive fraction of 0.40 (see text).

(d) Assumes a reproductive fraction of 0.25 (see text).

(e) The value used in the current ICRP recommendations.

(f) Value also assumed to apply to the fetus and children (see Chapter 6).

With data relating to five of these indicators, a regression analysis was performed in order to estimate the minimum gametic doubling doses for acute irradiation at various probability levels. Table 5.5 illustrates these doses calculated at a 95% probability level and it may be seen that minimal doubling doses estimated in this way ranged from 0.05 to 2.27 Sv. On the assumption of random fluctuation of the calculated regressions around some positive value (ie that there is a small but definite genetic effect), combined estimates of doubling dose were obtained by a simple additive procedure incorporating estimates of the contributions from spontaneously arising mutations. These calculations yielded a lower estimate of acute doubling dose of 1.69 Sv and an upper estimate of 2.23 Sv; application of a dose rate reduction factor of two then gave a chronic doubling dose estimate of 3.38–4.46 Sv (Neel et al[3]).

Indicator trait	Minimal doubling dose range (Sv)
Untoward pregnancy outcome	0.18–0.29
F1 mortality	0.68–1.10
F1 cancer	0.05–0.11
Sex chromosome aneuploidy	1.60
Mutations at protein loci	2.27

TABLE 5.5
Estimates of the doubling doses for hereditary effects excluded at the 95% confidence level by genetic data from the Japanese atomic bomb survivor studies (from Neel et al[3])

19   While it should be stressed that the estimates of genetic risk derived by the above analyses are subject to a number of assumptions and thereby carry considerable uncertainty, it is noteworthy that they fall within the upper range of doubling doses obtained from animal data. Possible explanations for this have been discussed[3,6,7,12] and central to these is the suggestion that some of the genetic endpoints employed in animal studies may be unusually responsive to radiation. It is now believed that the majority of radiation–induced mutations in mouse germ cells and mammalian somatic cells *in vitro* are DNA deletions/rearrangements and that radiation may only weakly induce DNA base pair changes (point mutations) in genes. A recent analysis of the available data on the molecular basis of human genetic diseases suggests that perhaps 50% of characterised Mendelian disorders present in the population are associated with DNA base pair changes and the remainder with deletions of varying extent[6]. The paucity of gene deletions in many such disorders implies therefore that a significant proportion of human genetic disease may be relatively unresponsive to radiation. For example, DNA deletion events in some genes may not be tolerated or be strongly selected against. Thus, the use of the total prevalence of genetic disorders (only half of which may be responsive to radiation) in the risk equation will tend to overestimate the projected frequency of induced mutation.

20   These arguments imply that a radiation doubling dose of 1 Gy for all genetic effects is likely to overestimate risk but, again, this view should be tempered by the fact that knowledge in this whole area is limited.

Congenital abnormalities and multifactorial diseases

21   Congenital abnormalities are represented by a heterogeneous group of disorders manifest at birth and include neural tube defects, cardiac abnormalities, and cleft lip/palate conditions. Approximately 50% of the total prevalence of these conditions has been suggested to be of multifactorial origin but in only a minority is there a defined genetic component. Other multifactorial diseases are the common conditions of adult life such as schizophrenia, multiple sclerosis, hypercholesterolemia/coronary heart disease, asthma, glaucoma and diabetes mellitus. Overall, these multifactorial conditions present with varying severity and are usually aetiologically complex, having unknown relative contributions from genetic and environmental factors. In the case of congenital malformations, however, it has been shown conclusively that irradiation of parental mice leads to malformations in offspring and that some of these traits may be transmitted to later generations[17,18].

22   With regard to these disorders, the central and contentious issues for radiological protection are:

(i)   their prevalence,
(ii) their genetic component,
(iii) the responsiveness of that genetic component to newly induced mutation.

23   Prevalence of congenital abnormalities at birth was found to be 4.3% and 6.0% in British Columbian (Canada) and Hungarian studies, respectively[2,19,20]. Other studies (see, for example, Chung and Myranthopoulos[21]) have yielded somewhat different incidences, probably reflecting the clinical criteria used for diagnosis and highlighting some of the problems faced in estimating the overall frequency of these conditions in the population. Recent data indicate that congenital abnormalities constitute between 1% and 2% of live births in the UK, although these figures exclude hip defects and minor malformations of the face and external genitalia[22,23]. Overall, the natural incidence of congenital defects in the population may be estimated to be in the range 1%–3% rising perhaps to 5%–6% with the inclusion of minor and somewhat uncertain malformations. The incidence of malformation in stillbirths is significantly higher[22,23].

24   Such problems of ascertainment become even more acute in the case of multifactorial diseases, particularly those manifesting in later life. A prevalence figure of 65% suggested in the Hungarian study[24] is widely quoted but subject to considerable uncertainty. To a large extent it probably reflects the view that, in the absence of random accidents or most acute infections, all deaths are associated with diseases that have some genetic component.

25   The data cited above have been used by UNSCEAR[2,13] to derive an overall prevalence of 6.0% for congenital abnormalities (at birth) and 65% for other multifactorial disorders. BEIR[4] adopted a prevalence of 2%–3% for congenital abnormalities and suggested a prevalence of 120% for other multifactorials (ie > 1 disorder per individual); however, BEIR did not provide risk estimates for this latter category. ICRP[5] tentatively assumed a prevalence of 70% in its calculations of risk of multifactorial disease and also stressed the uncertainties involved[16].

26   The mutational component of multifactorial disease is highly uncertain and doubtless varies amongst these disorders. UNSCEAR[1,14] assumed a 5% mutational component but with the revision of the estimates of prevalence in 1988 did not feel that this was appropriate and made no risk estimates. In 1980 BEIR used a range of 5%–50% for mutational components[15] while in 1990 BEIR adopted a range of 5%–35% in the case of congenital abnormalities[4]. ICRP[5] in its tentative calculations assumed a 'reasonable value' of 5% for the mutational component but suggested weighting for severity, ie the risk probability with a doubling dose of 1 Gy should be reduced by one-third and suggested further weighting in proportion to years of life lost. Sankaranarayanan[16] has recently discussed the effects of using different prevalences and mutational components in risk estimates, stressing the influence of these judgements and the large uncertainties involved.

27   Of equal uncertainty is the question of the responsiveness of multifactorial diseases to newly induced mutation. In a few conditions, eg diabetes and hypercholesterolemia, there is some evidence on the mutations involved but even here the apparent contribution of genetic and environmental factors appears to be variable. Also, the anomalously high frequency of some multifactorial diseases in some populations has led to suggestions that there may have been some selective advantage for such disease states in earlier periods of human history. Furthermore, the existing variability in the expression of these conditions appears to be so high that new mutations appearing in the population as a consequence of radiation exposure might be expected to have little or no impact on frequencies.

Conclusions

28   There remain many uncertainties in the formulation of risk estimates for the induction of genetic effects in man by radiation. The principal reasons for this are

(i)   the absence of directly informative human epidemiological data,
(ii) doubts on the relative responsiveness and hence appropriateness of some of the genetic endpoints employed in experimental animal studies.

In the case of single gene and chromosomal mutations animal data have been used to project genetic risks to man but it may be argued that these extrapolations are likely to overestimate overall genetic risk. Uncertainties in genetic risk estimates are at their greatest in the case of multifactorial diseases. For this complex group of disorders it is clear that a lack of fundamental knowledge greatly limits the capacity to provide soundly based estimates of risk.

RISK COEFFICIENTS

29   Whilst current uncertainties are recognised the coefficients that have been used by the Board for assessing the risks of genetic effects at low dose rates for a UK population are derived according to ICRP[5] and shown in Table 5.4b. These are considered to provide as reasonable an estimate of the risk as is possible based on the information currently available.

30   For the total population with a mean reproductive age of 30 years and an average life expectancy of 75 years the genetically significant dose is 0.4 (30/75) of that received by the population in a lifetime.

Mendelian and chromosomal genetic disorders

31   For genetic disease induced by radiation UNSCEAR[2] recommends a value of 120 cases of genetic disorder in all generations in 10^4 live births per Gy of low LET radiation

following exposure of either parent, thus providing a risk coefficient of $1.2 \ 10^{-2} \ Sv^{-1}$ (Table 5.4a). For the total population the genetically significant risk, ie that occurring prior to reproduction, is

$$0.4 \text{ of } 1.2 \ 10^{-2} \ Sv^{-1} = 0.5 \ 10^{-2} \ Sv^{-1}$$

For the determination of risk in the first two generations ICRP assumes that a large fraction of the equilibrium risk will be expressed in each of the first two generations as dominant or X-linked disorders; for this the value of 32 cases per 10^4 births per Gy (low LET) is used[2] ($0.32 \ 10^{-2} \ Gy^{-1}$, Table 5.4a). Thus, for the reproductive population the risk in the first two generations is rounded to $0.3 \ 10^{-2} \ Sv^{-1}$ and the corresponding risk for the total population is

$$0.4 \text{ of } 0.3 \ 10^{-2} \ Sv^{-1} = 0.1 \ 10^{-2} \ Sv^{-1}$$

Multifactorial disorders

32   ICRP has made the following assumption in its estimation of risk of these complex disorders:

(i)   that the natural prevalence is 70% (paragraph 25),
(ii)   that the mutational component is 5% (paragraph 26),
(iii) that the doubling dose for low LET radiation is 1 Gy (paragraphs 16–20).

33   On this basis the risk of these disorders at equilibrium is given by

$$0.7 \times 1/1 \times 0.05 = 3.5 \ 10^{-2} \ Sv^{-1}$$

In order to allow for the lower overall severity of these disorders compared with Mendelian and chromosomal disorders ICRP suggests a somewhat arbitrary weighting factor of one-third. Thus, severity weighted risk for the reproductive population in all generations is

$$3.5 \ 10^{-2} \ Sv^{-1} \times 1/3 = 1.2 \ 10^{-2} \ Sv^{-1}$$

Correspondingly, for the whole population the risk in all generations is

$$0.4 \times 1.2 \ 10^{-2} \ Sv^{-1} = 0.5 \ 10^{-2} \ Sv^{-1}$$

For the determination of risk in the first two generations ICRP further assumes that approximately 10% of the equilibrium risk will be expressed in each of the first two generations. Thus, for the reproductive population the *first* generation risk is

$$0.1 \times 1.2 \ 10^{-2} \ Sv^{-1} = 0.12 \ 10^{-2} \ Sv^{-1}$$

and the *second* generation risk is

$$0.1 \times (1.2 - 0.12) \ 10^{-2} \ Sv^{-1} = 0.11 \ 10^{-2} \ Sv^{-1}$$

The sum of these risks is $0.23 \ 10^{-2} \ Sv^{-1}$. With the same computational method the corresponding summed risk in the whole population over the first two generations is

$$0.09 \ 10^{-2} \ Sv^{-1} \qquad (0.23 \ 10^{-2} \ Sv^{-1} \times 0.4)$$

Overall genetic risks

34 Summation of genetic risks calculated as above provides a total genetic risk estimate in the reproductive population in all generations of $2.4 \ 10^{-2} \ Sv^{-1}$ and in the first two generations of $0.53 \ 10^{-2} \ Sv^{-1}$. The corresponding risks in the total population are $1.0 \ 10^{-2} \ Sv^{-1}$ and $0.19 \ 10^{-2} \ Sv^{-1}$, respectively (Table 5.4b). The total population risk estimate for all generations of $1.0 \ 10^{-2} \ Sv^{-1}$ (comprising $0.5 \ 10^{-2} \ Sv^{-1}$ for mendelian and chromosomal genetic disorders and $0.5 \ 10^{-2} \ Sv^{-1}$ for multifactional disorders) is the value used in current ICRP recommendations.

Risks in a working population

35 For a working population of ages 18 to 65 years and a reproductive interval of 18–30 years the reproductive working fraction is $(30 - 18)/(65 - 18) \cong 0.25$. Thus all genetic risk coefficients for working populations may be simply derived by multiplying risk coefficients for the reproductive population by 0.25, eg overall genetic risk in all generations is given by

$$2.4 \ 10^{-2} \ Sv^{-1} \times 0.25 = 0.6 \ 10^{-2} \ Sv^{-1} \qquad \text{(Table 5.4b)}$$

PARENTAL EXPOSURE AND CANCER IN OFFSPRING

36 The identification of spontaneously arising human germ line mutations that predispose offspring to tumorigenesis (see Chapter 2) has raised questions regarding the frequency at which such mutations may arise following radiation exposure.

37 Nomura[17,25] has reported on the incidence of tumours (principally lung adenomas but also leukaemias) in the offspring of X-irradiated mice where, at doses up to about 5 Gy, the first generation progeny of exposed animals showed a dose-dependent increase in tumour incidence. In these studies a tumour incidence of about 30% was seen at 5 Gy representing a six-fold increase in frequency over that of the unirradiated control group. Furthermore, in mating experiments with tumour bearing animals it was shown that the induced 'tumour mutations' were dominantly inherited with about 40% penetrance. These data imply that the rate of induction of tumour mutations in these mouse strains (about 3% Sv^{-1}) is significantly greater than that for other known genetic loci[26]. The design and interpretation of these studies have been discussed by a number of authors[6,10,27].

38 In man there are two major studies that require comment upon the possible induction of germ line tumour mutations by radiation.

39 A recent analysis for possible excess genetic effects in the first generation (F1) offspring of survivors of the Japanese atomic bombings yielded no evidence for a statistically significant excess of malignancy in these children[28,29]. Tumour assessment amongst F1 offspring (31 150) of irradiated parents (average gonadal dose of 0.43 Sv) yielded 43 malignancies (16 leukaemias and 27 non-leukaemias) while 49 malignancies (17 leukaemias and 32 non-leukaemias) were ascertained in 41 066 controls (Table 5.6a). However, data from the control group suggested that a maximum of 5% of the childhood malignancies observed might have a significant genetic determinant. Thus, specific examples of radiation-induced tumour mutations might be obscured by the natural frequency of sporadic malignancy.

40 The essentially negative findings from the Japanese study may be contrasted with the findings of Gardner et al[30] regarding a possible link between paternal occupational exposure to radiation at the Sellafield nuclear reprocessing plant (west Cumbria, UK) and leukaemia incidence in the offspring. This case–control study included 52 cases of leukaemia, 22 cases of non-Hodgkin's lymphoma (NHL) and 23 cases of Hodgkin's lymphoma in people of over 25 years born in west Cumbria and with dates of diagnosis between 1950 and 1985. Age and sex matched controls (1001) without these malignancies were derived from the same register as the cases. Analysis for paternal occupation revealed that 10 out of 64 of the ascertained fathers of leukaemia/NHL cases were employed at the Sellafield plant, while for the controls the figures were 54 and 383, respectively. The authors then found that 4 out of 10 of the case fathers had accumulated doses of 100 mSv or more before conception of their children, while the corresponding figure for the controls was 3 out of 54. There also appeared to be an association for those fathers receiving 10 mSv or more in the 6 months prior to conception. While these associations do not provide evidence of causality they would, at face value, imply a relative risk at these doses of 6–8 which broadly translates to an absolute risk of approximately a 1 in 300 chance of leukaemia in the F1 offspring compared to a national (sporadic) average of about 1 in 2000 (Table 5.6b)[26]. These findings clearly conflict both with current estimates of the risk of induced hereditary effects in man (Table 5.4b) and also with the lack of evidence for naturally occurring human mutations that predispose to leukaemia. These inconsistencies have been widely discussed[12,26,27,31-34] and Table 5.7 illustrates the divergence in doubling doses for F1 leukaemia that has been calculated from human and mouse data. Comparison of the data of Table 5.7 with those of Table 5.6 shows that while the mouse F1 leukaemia doubling doses as calculated are not wholly irreconcilable with those determined for

TABLE 5.6a
Childhood cancer in offspring (< 20 years and born in 1946–82) of the Japanese atomic bomb survivors *

	Number of children	Cancer cases	
		Leukaemia	Non-leukaemia
Irradiated	31 150	16	27
Controls	41 066	17	32
Relative risk		1.24	1.11

* Average parental dose of 435 mSv.

TABLE 5.6b
Extrapolation of Sellafield leukaemia risk to children of the Japanese atomic survivors

Observed Sellafield leukaemia risk at 150 mSv* average paternal dose	Projected leukaemia risk at 435 mSv	Leukaemia in 31 150 children of Japanese atomic bomb survivors receiving 435 mSv average parental dose	
		Predicted	Observed†
1 in 300	1 in 103	302	16

* Gardner et al[30] and Greaves[26].
† Yoshimoto et al[29].

other genetic indicators in the mouse, the F1 leukaemia doubling dose range implied by the west Cumbrian (Sellafield) data is widely divergent.

	Doses received (mSv)	Doubling dose (mSv)
Mouse – strain ICR		
Spermatogonia	360–5040	No excess
Spermatozoa and spermatids	360–5040	450
Mouse – strain N5		
Spermatogonia	5040	260
Man – Japanese studies		
Spermatogonia	435	No excess
Man – Sellafield study		
All spermatogenic stages	≥100	≥33
Post-spermatogonial stages	≥10	≥2.5

TABLE 5.7
Leukaemia in F1 progeny following paternal irradiation (from Nomura[35])

Note See Nomura[35] for computation and discussion.

41   Given the relatively small number of leukaemia cases recorded in the offspring of the Japanese atomic bomb survivors and in those of workers at the Sellafield plant, Little[36,37] has analysed the two data sets to see whether they are statistically compatible. He concluded that they are not, irrespective of whether the analyses are based on exposures during the whole of the pre-conception period or on doses received in the 6 month period prior to conception. Sensitivity analyses also showed that these findings are reasonably robust to uncertainties in dose estimates and to possible under-ascertainment of leukaemia cases[37]. Also, in a recent study the pre-conception dose histories of men occupationally exposed to radiation at a nuclear facility in Canada were compared with the incidence of leukaemia in their offspring[38]. Whilst providing no support for the Gardner hypothesis this study may not have the statistical power to discriminate between the risks found by Gardner *et al* and those that apply in the case of the Japanese atomic bomb survivors. Studies performed in the vicinity of the Dounreay plant in northern Scotland[39] and the Aldermaston and Burghfield plants in southern England[40] have also lacked the statistical power to distinguish between the risks reported by Gardner *et al*[30] for pre-conception exposure and the atomic bomb data.

42   An additional comparison between the leukaemia incidence recorded in the children of Japanese atomic bomb survivors (Table 5.6a) and that which might be predicted on the basis of the absolute leukaemia risk estimated from the Gardner *et al* data (Table 5.6b) more straightforwardly illustrates the degree of uncertainty faced in the interpretation of the Sellafield findings.

43   It is unclear whether the Gardner *et al* data should or should not be interpreted as indicating that parental irradiation increases the risk of childhood leukaemia in offspring and for this reason the Board does not include the postulated effect in its current

estimates of genetic risk. Although the genetics of most forms of cancer predisposing mutation in man are simple this is not always so and even for sporadically arising disease poorly understood germ line processes can in some instances influence cancer development[41-43]; the extent to which these genetic uncertainties affect the interpretation of the Gardner *et al*[30] and Nomura[25] data remains, however, a matter of speculation. There are other animal data which imply that tumour predisposition in offspring can be a consequence of chemical[44,45] or radiation[46] exposure of parental animals; as yet, however, the fundamental genetics of such induced predisposition remain obscure. Overall, the general principle of radiation-induced germ line mutation predisposing to neoplasia in offspring is not unsound: what is in question is the degree of transmitted risk at low doses and whether unusual germ line mutational processes may play a role[34,45]. In recognising the paucity of informative data on this potentially important problem the Board has emphasised the need for further epidemiological and genetic studies to resolve the outstanding problems of interpretation and will make future recommendations in the light of new data[27]. In particular, more powerful epidemiological information will come from a large study, currently in progress, to link the UK National Registry for Radiation Workers (see Appendix B) to national databases of childhood cancer[47].

CONCLUSIONS

44   Data relevant to radiation-induced heritable effects in man have been reviewed and emphasis has been placed on the difficulties of extrapolating existing data on experimental animals to man. The estimation of doubling doses for genetic effects is of particular concern and current uncertainties on this are discussed in the light of recent re-analyses of the genetic data from offspring of the Japanese atomic bomb survivors. Consideration is also given to new data on the fundamental nature of radiation-induced germ line mutations and their implications for the relative radiosensitivity of genetic endpoints. Recent discussions of the question whether risk coefficients derived from existing animal data might overestimate the genetic effects of radiation in man are also outlined. For the present, however, it is thought appropriate to apply the risk coefficients recommended by ICRP[5] for low dose rate, low LET exposures. Thus, the risk of genetic disease in the reproductive population over all generations is calculated to be $2.4 \ 10^{-2} \ Gy^{-1}$; for the whole population the risk will be 40% of this, ie $1.0 \ 10^{-2} \ Gy^{-1}$; for a working population the risk will be about 25% of this, ie $0.6 \ 10^{-2} \ Gy^{-1}$. For high dose/high dose rate exposures (see Chapter 8) these risk coefficients should be increased by a factor of three.

45   Data relevant to parental exposure to radiation and cancer in the offspring are also discussed with particular regard to the great uncertainties faced in the interpretation of both human epidemiological data and animal data. It is concluded that, in view of these uncertainties, it would at present be inappropriate specifically to apply these data in the estimation of genetic risks.

REFERENCES

1   UNSCEAR. Sources and effects of ionizing radiation. 1977 Report to the General Assembly, with annexes. New York, United Nations (1977).

2   UNSCEAR. Sources, effects and risks of ionizing radiation. 1988 Report to the General Assembly, with annexes. New York, United Nations (1988).

3   Neel, J V, Schull, W J, Awa, A A, Satoh, C, Kato, H, Otake, M, and Yoshimoto, Y. The children of parents exposed to atomic bombs: Estimates of the genetic doubling dose of radiation for humans. *Am. J. Hum. Genet.*, **46**, 1053–72 (1990).

4   BEIR V. Health effects of exposure to low levels of ionizing radiation. Washington DC, NAS/NRC (1990).

5   ICRP. 1990 Recommendations of the International Commission on Radiological Protection. ICRP Publication 60, *Ann. ICRP*, **21**, Nos 1–3 (1991).

6   Sankaranarayanan, K. Ionising radiation and genetic risks. IV Current methods, estimates of risk of Mendelian disease, human data and lessons from biochemical and molecular studies of mutations. *Mutat. Res.*, **258**, 99–122 (1991).

7   Neel, J V. An estimate of the doubling dose of ionising radiation for humans. IN *Proceedings Workshop on Genetic Effects of Ionising Radiations* (Eds C D J Ter Marsch and N E Gentner). Chalk River, AECL, pp 23–7 (1990).

8   Neel, J V, and Lewis, S B. The comparative radiation genetics of humans and mice. *Ann. Rev. Genet.*, **24**, 327–62 (1990).

9   Ehling, U H. Methods to estimate genetic risk. IN *Mutations in Man* (Ed G Obe). Berlin, Springer, pp 291–318 (1984).

10 Selby, P B. Experimental induction of dominant mutations in mammals by ionising radiations and chemicals. *Issue. Rev. Teratol.*, **5**, 181–253 (1990).

11 McKusick, V A. *Mendelian Inheritance in Man* (9th Edition). Baltimore, John Hopkins University Press (1990).

12 Neel, J V. Update on the genetic effects of ionizing radiation. *JAMA*, **266**, 698–701 (1991).

13 UNSCEAR. Genetic and somatic effects of ionizing radiation. 1986 Report to the General Assembly, with annexes. New York, United Nations (1986).

14 UNSCEAR. Ionizing radiation: Sources and biological effects. 1982 Report to the General Assembly, with annexes. New York, United Nations (1982).

15 BEIR III. The effects on populations of exposure to low levels of ionizing radiation. Washington DC, NAS/NRC (1980).

16 Sankaranarayanan, K. Genetic effects of ionising radiation in man. *Ann. ICRP*, **22**, 75–94 (1991).

17 Nomura, T. Parental exposure to x-rays and chemicals induces heritable tumours and anomalies in mice. *Nature*, **296**, 575–7 (1982).

18 Lyon, M, and Renshaw, R. Induction of congenital malformation in mice by parental irradiation: Transmission to later generations. *Mutat. Res.*, **198**, 277–83 (1988).

19 Trimble, B K, and Doughty, J H. The amount of hereditary disease in human populations. *Ann. Hum. Genet.*, **38**, 199–222 (1974).

20 Czeizel, A E, and Sankaranarayanan, K. The load of genetic and partially genetic disorders in man. I Congenital anomalies: Estimates of detriment in terms of lost and impaired life. *Mutat. Res.*, **128**, 73–103 (1984).

21 Chung, C S, and Myranthopoulos, N C. Factors affecting risk of congenital malformations in birth defects. *Orig. Art. Series*, **XI** No. 10 (1975).

22 OPCS. Congenital malformation statistics – notifications. London, HMSO, Series MB3 (1990).

23 OPCS. Congenital malformation statistics – notifications. London, HMSO, Series MB3 (1992).

24 Czeizel, A E, Sankaranarayanan, K, Losonci, A, Rudas, T, and Keresztes, M. The load of genetic and partially genetic diseases in man. II Some selected common multifactorial diseases: Estimates of population prevalence and of detriment in terms of lost and impaired life. *Mutat. Res.*, **176**, 259–92 (1988).

25 Nomura, T. Further studies on x-ray and chemically induced germ line alterations causing tumours and malformations in mice. IN *Genetic Toxicology of Environmental Chemicals*, Part B (Eds C Ramel, B Lambert and J Magnusson). New York, Alan R Liss, pp 13–30 (1986).

26 Greaves, M F. The Sellafield childhood leukaemia cluster: Are germ line mutations responsible? *Leukaemia*, **4**, 391–6 (1990).

27 NRPB. NRPB/HSE Workshop: Follow-up to Professor Gardner's case-control study of leukaemia and lymphoma among young people near Sellafield nuclear plant in West Cumbria. Chilton, NRPB-M248 (1990).

28   Yoshimoto, Y, Neel, J V, Schull, W J, Kato, H, Makuchi, K, Soda, M, Eto, R, and Mabuchi, K.   Malignant tumours during the first two decades of life in the offspring of atomic bomb survivors. *Am. J. Hum. Genet.*, **46**, 1041–52 (1990).

29   Yoshimoto, Y, Neel, J V, Schull, W J, Kato, H, Soda, M, Eto, R, and Mabuchi, K. Frequency of malignant tumours during the first two decades of life in the offspring (F1) of atomic bomb survivors. Hiroshima, Radiation Effects Research Foundation, Report TR4-90 (1990).

30   Gardner, M J, Snee, M P, Hall, A J, Powell, C A, Downes, S, and Terrell, J D. Results of case-control study of leukaemia and lymphoma among young people near Sellafield nuclear plant in West Cumbria. *Br. Med. J.*, **300**, 423–9 (1990).

31   Evans, H J. Leukaemia and radiation. *Nature*, **345**, 16–17 (1990).

32   Narod, S A. Radiation, genetics and childhood leukaemia. *Eur. J. Cancer*, **26**, 661–4 (1990).

33   Abrahamson, S. Childhood leukaemia at Sellafield. *Radiat. Res.*, **123**, 237–8 (1990).

34   Cox, R. Transgeneration carcinogenesis: Are there genes that break the rules? *Radiol. Prot. Bull.* No. 129, 15–23 (1992).

35   Nomura, T. Of mice and men? *Nature*, **345**, 671 (1990).

36   Little, M P. A comparison between the risks of childhood leukaemia from parental exposure to radiation in the Sellafield workforce and those displayed among the Japanese atomic bomb survivors. *J. Radiol. Prot.*, **10**, 185–98 (1990).

37   Little, M P. A comparison of the apparent risks of childhood leukaemia from parental exposure to radiation in the six months prior to conception in the Sellafield workforce and the Japanese bomb survivors. *J. Radiol. Prot.*, **11**, 77–90 (1991).

38   McLaughlin, J R, Anderson, T W, Clarke, E A, and King, W. Occupational exposure of fathers to ionizing radiation and the risks of leukaemia in offspring – a case-control study. Canada, AECB-INFO 0424 (1992).

39   Urquhart, J D, Black, R J, Muirhead, M J, Sharp, L, Maxwell, M, Eden, O B, and Adams Jones, D. Case-control study of leukaemia and non-Hodgkin's lymphoma in children in Caithness near the Dounreay nuclear installation. *Br. Med. J.*, **302**, 687–92 (1991).

40   Roman, E, Watson, A, Beral, V, Buckle, S, Bull, D, Baker, K, Ryder, H, and Barton, C. Case-control study of leukaemia and non-Hodgkin's lymphoma among children aged 0–4 years living in West Berkshire and North Hampshire health districts. *Br. Med. J.*, **306**, 615–21 (1993).

41   Scrable, H J, Sapienza, Ć, and Cavanee, W K. Genetic and epigenetic losses of heterozygosity in cancer predisposition and progression. *Adv. Cancer Res.*, **54**, 25 (1990).

42   Ponder, B A. Inherited predisposition to cancer. *Trend. Genet.*, **6**, 213–8 (1990).

43   Haas, O A, Argyriou-Tirita, A, and Lion, T. Parental origin of chromosomes involved in the translocation t(9;22). *Nature*, **359**, 414–16 (1992).

44   Tomatis, L, Cabral, J R P, Likhachev, A J, and Ponomarkov, V. Increased cancer incidence in the progeny of male rates exposed to ethyl nitro source before mating. *Int. J. Cancer*, **28**, 475–8 (1981).

45   Tomatis, L, Narod, S, and Yamasaki, H. Transgeneration transmission of carcinogenic risk. *Carcinogenesis*, **13**, 145–151 (1992).

46   Takahashi, T, Watanabe, H, Dohi, K, and Ito, A. ^{252}Cf relative biological effectiveness and inheritable effect of fission neutrons in mouse liver tumorigenesis. *Cancer Res.*, **52**, 1948–53 (1992).

47   Draper, G J, Kendall, G M, Muirhead, C R, Sorahan, T, Fox, A J, and Kinlen, L J. Cancer in the children of radiation workers. *Radiol. Prot. Bull.*, No. 129, 10–14 (1992).

6 Irradiation *in utero*

INTRODUCTION

1   The developing embryo and fetus may be more sensitive to some effects of radiation than other age groups in the population. The most important such effects are severe mental retardation and cancer induction. The risk of hereditary disease is taken to be the same for *in utero* irradiation as after birth[1,2]. The types of effect described below encompass those where a dose threshold is likely (malformations and severe mental retardation) and stochastic effects (cancer and hereditary disease). While the quantitative data on radiation–induced malformations and hereditary disease are largely derived from animal studies, human data provide the basis for assessment of mental retardation and cancer risks.

EMBRYONIC AND FETAL DEVELOPMENT

2   Ovulation generally occurs around the midpoint of the menstrual cycle, rarely earlier than 10 days after the first day of the preceding menstrual cycle. Thus, fertilisation of the ovum by a spermatozoon to form the single cell zygote that eventually gives rise to a new individual typically occurs around 2 weeks into the menstrual cycle. Fertilisation takes place in the uterine tube and is followed by a series of zygotic cell cleavages (cell divisions) but with no increase in overall mass. Such cleavage proceeds until the 16–32 cell stage, the morula, is reached at around 1 week post-conception. Up to the 4–8 cell stage it seems, from animal studies, that each cell remains pluripotent and, alone, is able to complete the full developmental cycle. This pluripotency appears to be lost around the point at which the morula undergoes a cellular reorganisation where inner and outer cell masses become apparent. The inner mass provides the cells that give rise to the embryo *per se* while the outer mass forms a structure termed the trophoblast which acts to provide a nutrient supply to the developing embryo. The blastocyst, thus formed, passes to the uterus where it becomes implanted into the uterine lining. This implantation process prompts a local reorganisation of the uterine endometrium to form early placental structures which act to supply the developing embryo with maternally derived oxygen and nutrients. The whole period encompassing fertilisation and completion of implantation occupies around 2 weeks.

3   Further embryonic development is characterised by substantial increase in embryonic mass and commences around 3 weeks after conception. The inner cell mass separates to form the endoderm and ectoderm layers which adopt a two disc structure (the embryonic disc). The space between the ecoderm and the trophoblast forms the amniotic cavity while endoderm cells flatten and spread to form a lining to a cavity termed the primary yolk sac. Ectodermal cells then begin further proliferation and differentiation and the first major structure to emerge is the 'primitive streak' which expands to form a pear-shaped body along the central axis of the embryonic disc; this is

followed by the appearance of other embryonic structures from which all the body organs derive. This period of early organogenesis proceeds during the 4–8 week period following conception; importantly, the initiation of development of the forebrain occurs late in this period.

4   The transition from embryonic to fetal developmental phases may be considered to occur around the eighth to ninth week; this is not a distinct phase change and simply denotes the time at which distinct human characteristics emerge. Further growth, development and maturation of fetal organs and organ systems continues to birth at around week 38.

5   The above outline serves to demonstrate the complexity of developmental processes and it may be estimated that perhaps 30%–50% of conceptuses are subject to spontaneous abortion, usually very early in development, by means of poorly understood natural mechanisms designed to eliminate such errors[3]. Of the remaining live-born it has been estimated that around 6% carry some form of congenital abnormality[2], although the frequency of such abnormal births is somewhat dependent on the clinical criteria used. Genetic, maternal and environmental factors all contribute towards spontaneous abortion and fetal abnormality. In the case of congenital abnormalities in the live-born around 10% are believed to be of genetic origin, 60% due to environmental and genetic factors combined (multifactorial), while the remainder are of unknown origin.

Lethal effects

6   Animal studies[4,5] indicate that the pre-implantation embryo exhibits the greatest sensitivity to the lethal effects of radiation and, in mice and rats, increased mortality has been observed following 0.10–0.15 Gy low LET exposure on the first day of gestation. At the single cell stage it may be expected that embryo-lethal effects will be linearly related to dose but, with increasing cellularity and subsequent organogenesis, LD_{50} values will tend to increase through gestation and be characterised by a threshold type response with threshold values progressively increasing from about 0.1 Gy to about 1 Gy at term. For the later phases of gestation LD_{50} values of 1–2 Gy should be expected.

Malformations and other developmental effects

7   Malformations result from cell killing during the active phase of cell proliferation and differentiation during organogenesis. The nature of the malformation is determined by the particular phase of organogenesis at the time of exposure. In rodents and the monkey functional and behavioral effects have also been demonstrated[6]. Mental retardation has been observed in humans exposed *in utero* and is discussed separately (paragraphs 18–41). Growth disturbances (without malformation) are the more likely result of irradiation later in pregnancy[4,7,8].

8   *In utero* irradiation during the period of early organogenesis has been shown to cause a range of malformations, depending on the timing of exposure, in every mammalian species tested[4,6]. Defects in the skeletal and central nervous systems, and in the eye, commonly occur. Given the capacity of the embryo to replace damaged cells, it is to be expected that a threshold will apply for the induction of malformation as a result of the inactivation of a number of cells, during the development of a particular organ. Dose–response relationships from animal studies are usually curvilinear, sometimes with an apparent threshold, sometimes merging into background incidence. The early phases of human development, including organogenesis, are more similar to

those in other mammalian species than is the late (fetal) period. While it is generally accepted that thresholds are also likely to apply for induction of malformation in humans[4,9] there is debate about their values. Thus thresholds of 0.25 Gy up to 28 days gestation and 0.5 Gy from day 50 onwards have been suggested by UNSCEAR[2], based on Brent[10], but questioned by Mole[11] who suggested a range of 0.4–2.0 Gy. Mole also pointed to the importance, for radiation protection purposes, of the effect of dose protraction in further increasing the threshold value, to several gray.

9   There are no human data on radiation-induced malformation capable of providing dose–effect data, and precise threshold values cannot be determined. Reports exist of malformed offspring as a result of maternal radiotherapy during pregnancy (see, for example, reference 12). The doses involved were likely to have been several gray.

10   When the Board developed health effect models from the 1988 UNSCEAR Report (see NRPB-R226[13]) the only early effect considered to result from exposure of the pre-implantation conceptus was prenatal death. Experimental data suggested that irradiation at this stage either caused death or resulted in a normal fetus[14,15]. More recently, evidence has been presented of teratogenic effects resulting from pre-implantation irradiation of the mouse conceptus[5,16,17]. The usual dose employed was from 1 to 4 Gy, with preliminary evidence of a threshold in the range 0.5–1.0 Gy, for multicellular stages. However, these effects are limited to a particular mouse strain and furthermore relate to a malformation (gastroschisis) with very variable background incidence and which does not appear to be induced by irradiation during the period of organogenesis. It would therefore be inappropriate to utilise such results in considering human risks, rather than the animal data from different strains of mice and from rats, which show no such teratogenic effects from pre-implantation irradiation[14,18-20] (see also the review by Mole[11]). The most important acute effect of irradiation at this stage remains lethality. However, it is perhaps too simplistic to consider this an all-or-none response. Increased levels of chromosome aberrations have been reported in cells from mouse fetuses irradiated as zygotes, and attributed to radiation-induced instability of the genome[21]. The possibility of radiation-induced mutant cells contributing to embryonic mal-development (and cancer) has been suggested by Gaulden and Murry[22] who considered the first 6 weeks (and particularly the first 2 weeks) of development as the most susceptible period for such low dose effects.

11   Evidence of human malformations due to *in utero* irradiation is lacking from the follow-up of the Japanese atomic bomb survivors. However, Yamasaki[23] studied Nagasaki survivors 6 years after exposure and found a higher incidence of miscarriages, still-births, neo-natal and infant deaths, as well as a decrease in mean height and head circumference in offspring of cases who were within 2000 m of the hypocentre and suffered radiation sickness (dose estimated to be in excess of 0.5 Gy, based on the T65DR dosimetry system)[24] compared with cases within 2000 m but without sickness, and with controls considered not to have been exposed. Malformations may have been associated with both prenatal and neo-natal deaths, although possible effects of maternal ill-health and malnutrition must also be considered in this context, as well as for growth impairment[25,26]. There was some direct evidence of an increased incidence of malformations in 5 out of 17 surviving children in the affected group who suffered one or more of the following conditions: eye defects, urinary incontinence and mental retardation[25].

12   The difference in the extent to which malformations have been observed in the follow-up of the Japanese atomic bomb survivors and in animal studies may be explained by the fact that the short (20–30 day) susceptible period of organogenesis (beginning 3 to 4 weeks after conception) in the human comprises about 10% of total gestation, whereas in the mouse, for example, the susceptible period amounts to about 25% of the total. The small number of human embryos therefore likely to have been exposed during the appropriate period of organogenesis, to doses above the threshold for malformation but below that for lethality[4] would be insufficient to allow any resulting increase in the incidence of malformations to be detected against the prevailing background rate. The position is further complicated by the difficulty in arriving at figures for the natural incidence of congenital malformation. Values quoted by UNSCEAR[2] suggest about 6% of live births.

Conclusions

13   In the usual radiological protection situation, of low dose and low dose rate *in utero* exposures, it is most unlikely that the threshold dose for induction of malformation resulting from *in utero* exposure will be reached (see Table 6.1). Even for acute exposures in the most sensitive first month of pregnancy the threshold for malformation is probably not less than 250 mGy. It can be concluded that for low dose and low dose rate *in utero* exposures the risk of radiation-induced malformation must be very small compared with the natural, spontaneously arising risk. This conclusion is supported by such limited human evidence as exists on the effect of low dose X-irradiation *in utero* during the first trimester of pregnancy on the occurrence of congenital abnormalities. The value of most such studies is, however, compromised by size and/or methodology[28].

TABLE 6.1
*Deterministic effects
following low LET
irradiation of the
human embryo**

Embryonic age (weeks)	Minimal dose (Gy) for:		
	Lethality	Gross malformations	Mental retardation (Japanese data)
0–1	No threshold at day 1? 0.1 thereafter	No threshold at day 1?	No effects observed to about 8 weeks
2–5	0.25–0.5	0.2	
5–7	0.5	0.5	
7–21	> 0.5	Very few observed	Week 8–15: no threshold? Week 16–25: threshold dose 0.6–0.7 Gy
To term	> 1.0	Very few observed	Week 25–term: no effects observed

* Based on data cited in Brent *et al*[4], Müller and Streffer[5] and this report, utilising information from human epidemiological studies and animal experiments.

14   The possible contribution of somatic mutational damage to fetal malformation following irradiation in the first few weeks of pregnancy, cannot be clearly distinguished from the effects of cell killing. Thus, for example, in the application of medical diagnostic procedures, involving ionising radiation, in women of reproductive age, a small risk of somatic mutational damage to early embryonic cells resulting in malformation cannot be excluded.

GROWTH IMPAIRMENT

15   For mental retardation and growth impairment the susceptible period during human gestation is about four times longer than that for induction of malformation and there is, by contrast, clear evidence for both these effects in the offspring of the Japanese atomic bomb survivors. Small head size is the commonest manifestation of growth retardation in experimental animals and humans, and it is considered with mental retardation below. Other evidence of growth retardation consists of height and weight reduction. Reference has already been made to early findings by Yamasaki[23]. Subsequently a study was carried out of 17 year olds who had been exposed *in utero* at Hiroshima as well as Nagasaki[24] which showed evidence of a failure to achieve optimal growth (head circumference, height and weight) in those whose mothers had been exposed to 0.5 Gy or more compared with offspring of those with less, or no, exposure. At the doses involved microcephaly and mental retardation are more important effects.

16   The effect on growth of low dose *in utero* irradiation has been examined in three studies (see reference 28). Despite the small cohort size, one study[29] was considered by UNSCEAR[30] to demonstrate an effect on height at doses of only 2–70 mGy. However, the apparent effect was most pronounced in the first trimester, whereas *in utero* irradiation in the second and third trimesters had had a greater effect in 13 and 14 year old Nagasaki females[31] than did first trimester exposure.

Conclusion

17   It may be concluded that the data on growth impairment are inconclusive and insufficient to allow any firm conclusion.

RADIATION EFFECTS ON THE DEVELOPING BRAIN

18   The human brain is probably the most complex organ of the human body and its proper development and function depend on an elaborate sequence of events which must be coordinated temporally and spatially. Any disturbance of this sequence could lead to abnormal development since the normal function of the nervous system depends on the proper location of neuronal cells[2,32].

19   The main source of human information on the effects of prenatal irradiation on the developing nervous system comes from the follow-up of the atomic bomb survivors at Hiroshima and Nagasaki. This population provides information on the effects of exposure on a population exposed *in utero* to a wide range of doses and at varying stages of development.

Development of the brain

20   Most of the structural complexity of the brain develops in the fetal period through a series of events involving the production of neuronal cells, their migration from the periventricular zones of proliferation to the cortex, further differentiation, and their subsequent growth in size with the development of specific interneuronal connections. The migratory process is an active, timed phenomenon dependent to a large degree on an interaction between the surface membranes of the neurons and their guidance cells, and on the subsequent morphological shaping of the two principal types of cells that give rise to the cerebrum, the neurons and neuroglia[32,33]. The effects of radiation on the developing brain are closely related to its stage of development and it has become common practice to consider four stages, as follows.

(i)   In the first period (fertilisation to the seventh week) the precursors of the neurons and neuroglia have emerged and are mitotically active.

(ii) In the second period (8 to 15 weeks), a rapid increase in the number of neurons occurs; they migrate to their ultimate developmental sites in the cerebral cortex and lose their capacity to divide, becoming perennial cells. Synaptic contacts with other neurons start to develop.

(iii) In the third period (16–25 weeks), differentiation *in situ* accelerates, synaptogenesis that began about the eighth week increases, and the definitive cytoarchitecture of the brain unfolds.

(iv) The fourth period (26 weeks to term) is one of continued architectural and cellular differentiation and synaptogenesis of the cerebrum, with, at the same time, accelerated growth and development of the cerebellum.

Radiation effects on development

21   The Atomic Bomb Casualty Commission and its successor the Radiation Effects Research Foundation established a number of study populations that have been examined for radiation effects following prenatal exposure. In 1955 a comprehensive study group termed PE-86 was set up mainly from birth registrations, interviews of women in the genetics programme who were possibly pregnant at the time of the bombings, the national census of 1950, and other *ad hoc* censuses. No attempt was made to match exposed and control groups. In 1959 a revised PE-86 sample was established[34]. This population consists of two exposed groups who were within 2000 m (the proximally exposed) or between 3000 and 5000 m (the distally exposed) of the hypocentre of the explosions. These groups were matched for sex and age (by trimester of pregnancy).

22   The extended follow-up of the atomic bomb survivors has shown that a number of measures of radiation damage to the brain can be attributed to radiation damage *in utero*, and that the severity of damage depends on the stage of development. Where and how exposure to ionising radiation at sensitive developmental stages affects brain function is unclear at present. Observed effects could be due to cell killing, to an effect on cell migration or to an effect on cellular differentiation such as on the ability of neurons to establish proper synaptic connections[33,35].

23   The main effect of prenatal irradiation that has caused concern is an increase in the risk of severe mental retardation (SMR) but this is paralleled by loss of IQ, impaired school performance and, to a lesser extent, seizures and neuromuscular performance. Severe mental retardation has frequently been associated with reduced head size but there have also been some cases of small head size without apparent mental retardation. The data on severe mental retardation are restricted to the revised PE-86 sample, since it is the only group for whom extensive clinical follow-up information is

available for both cities. The intelligence test scores and school performance data were obtained on the PE-86 sample in 1955, before the revised sample was established.

24   Absorbed doses to the embryo or fetus are not yet available under the DS86 dosimetry, and may not be for some time. Published analyses of the effects of prenatal irradiation on the developing brain have therefore used the estimated dose to the mother's uterus on the DS86 dosimetry system as the basis for assessing dose–response relationships[33].

Severe mental retardation

25   In a study of 1544 children exposed *in utero* at Hiroshima and Nagasaki 30 cases of clinically diagnosed severe mental retardation (SMR) have been identified with a greater incidence than expected in the high dose groups*. Excess mental retardation was not observed following exposure up to 8 weeks from conception, was at a maximum between 8 and 15 weeks, was somewhat lower between 16 and 25 weeks, and no effect was observed for exposure after 25 weeks[37]. Of the 30 children with SMR, 18 (60%) had disproportionately small heads (ie a circumference less than two standard deviations below the mean for the group)[36], 3 cases had Down's syndrome (with doses of 0, 0.29 and 0.56 Gy), 1 case had Japanese encephalitis in infancy (dose 0.03 Gy), and 1 case had a retarded sibling (dose 0 Gy). The lack of any effect observed for exposures before 8 weeks does not necessarily imply that no damage occurs at this time, but if it does either it is of a much less severe nature or the damage to the fetus has been sufficient to cause its loss.

26   The period of maximum sensitivity corresponds with the timing of the major phases of neuronal proliferation and migration within the cerebral cortex, with two waves of neuronal migration occurring from the seventh to the tenth week and from the tenth to fifteenth week. Fetal brain damage at this time is likely, therefore, to result from damage to cell production and/or cell migration/differentiation. The majority of cell division in the proliferative zones has taken place by 16 weeks. Damage during the later 16–25 week period corresponds to the period when supporting structures are developing and connections between neuronal cells are established[2,32].

Intelligence tests

27   Methods of measuring intelligence are very variable and intelligence tests differ from one another in the weight given to various measures of performance. Despite this, most tests of intelligence give a distribution of results for a population that are (approximately) normally distributed (mean = 100) and with a standard deviation of between 14 and 16. Individuals whose scores lie less than two standard deviations below the mean are commonly described as retarded. On this basis a person with an IQ of less than 70 would be considered retarded and with an IQ of about 50 or less would be severely retarded. The probability of an SMR of 50 or less occurring by chance is about 1 in 2000.

28   Schull *et al*[38] have reported the results of intelligence test scores at 10–11 years of age of individuals exposed prenatally to the atomic bombings at Hiroshima and Nagasaki. The results closely parallel those of SMR with no evidence of a radiation-

---

*SMR is defined as those 'unable to perform simple calculations, to make conversation, to care for themselves, or if they are completely unmanageable or if they have been institutionalised'[36].

related effect on intelligence among those individuals exposed within 0–7 weeks after fertilisation or at times later than week 26. For those exposed at 8–15 weeks and to a lesser extent those exposed at 16–25 weeks, the mean tests scores suggest a progressive shift downwards in individual IQ scores with increasing exposure. For individuals exposed between 8 and 15 weeks the regression of intelligence score on estimated DS86 uterine absorbed dose corresponds on a linear model to 21 to 29 points at 1 Gy. For the 16–25 week group the shift in IQ is 10–21 points at 1 Gy.

School performance

29   A study on the history of school performance of 10–11 year old children prenatally exposed at Hiroshima and a suitable exposed comparison group has also been reported[39]. As judged by school performance, damage to the 8–15 week old fetal brain appears to be linearly related to fetal dose. Damage at 16–25 weeks appears similar to that seen in the 8–15 week group. In the groups exposed within the first 7 weeks of gestation or at times longer than 26 weeks no evidence of a radiation-related effect on school performance was found.

Seizures and neuromuscular performance

30   Both an increased incidence of unprovoked seizures[40] and a reduction in neuromuscular performance[41] have been observed in the atomic bomb survivors irradiated *in utero* in the sensitive 8–15 week period. However, the analyses were strongly influenced by inclusion of the cases of SMR and it is not clear to what extent these different endpoints are symptomatic of the same or different radiation-induced events in the brain[33].

Dose–response relationships

31   This series of studies on the atomic bomb survivors related to the effects of radiation on the developing brain all parallel each other. Although there are differences in the design of the studies they are consistent in suggesting that the period of greatest radiation sensitivity of the brain of the developing fetus is between 8 and 15 weeks of gestation, with a lower risk between 16 and 25 weeks. No damage is apparent after birth for exposures before 8 weeks and after 25 weeks. Although it is possible, it seems unlikely that all the effects observed are attributable to damage to precisely the same neuronal cells. It has also been suggested by Mole[42] that fetal exposure to external irradiation, resulting in the development of SMR, will have occurred concurrently with exposure of the mother. The development of a dose–response relationship based on fetal exposure must assume no maternal influence on the developing fetal brain. Mole[43] has proposed that anaemia of pregnant women, resulting from exposure to radiation, may have an indirect effect on the fetus. He has also suggested that at the doses received fetal erythropoiesis would be affected, which might result in diminished oxygen transport from placenta to fetus and that this could augment damage to the fetal brain[44]. For the present, however, these hypotheses remain to be tested experimentally.

32   There has been extensive debate over the shape of the dose–response relationship for severe mental retardation in the two sensitive periods of development and whether a threshold exists below which there is no effect. There must also be some question about the merits of fitting any dose response without some understanding of the cellular and tissue mechanisms responsible for the effect.

33   With the DS86 dosimetry the data on SMR for exposures in the most sensitive 8–15 week period are consistent with a linear dose response up to 1.5 Gy with a risk of about 0.43 Gy^{-1} (estimated SE= 0.087)[37]. The data also indicate that there could be a threshold; however, because of the paucity of data the estimation of the value of this threshold is not straightforward. When all the cases of SMR are included in the analysis the lower bound of the estimated threshold includes zero, ie a threshold cannot be shown to occur by statistical means. If, however, the two cases of Down's syndrome in the 8–15 week period are excluded (for which there is a strong argument) the 95% lower bound of the threshold appears to range from 0.12 to 0.23 Gy. If, however, these selected data are fitted with a linear dose response, with a threshold in this range, then the data suggest a risk of SMR of almost 100% Gy^{-1}. This is at variance with the observations although alternative models, such as a linear–quadratic, would give a better fit to the data[33].

34   The most appropriate model to fit the data therefore remains an open question in the absence of a clear mechanistic basis for the response. It would seem prudent for the present, however, to assume no threshold for SMR in this most sensitive 8–15 week period in fetal brain development.

35   The IQ data for the non-SMR children in Hiroshima and Nagasaki with exposures to atomic bomb radiation *in utero* 8–15 weeks post-conception are given by Schull *et al*[38]. Whilst IQs in the control group and the 0.10–0.49 Gy group do not appear to differ to a statistically significant extent, the mean IQ in the latter group is lower than that in the former and seems to be in line with a linear no-threshold model fitted across all the dose groups. A linear no-threshold model is consistent with the data, although other models such as a linear–quadratic model and a linear model with a threshold of 0.1 Gy also fit generally well. The only data point for which none of the above models fits too well is that for doses of 0.01–0.09 Gy, for which the mean IQ is slightly higher than in the controls. Removal of either this point or that for the controls would yield some improvement in the fit of these models. It is noted that the 'control' group includes both those with doses less than 0.01 Gy and those not in city (NIC) at the time of bombing. The inclusion of the NIC group, which was also performed for the SMR analysis, differs from the procedure for the analyses of cancer mortality, for which the NIC group was excluded on the basis that their cancer rates appeared to differ from those in the cities at the time of bombing. For SMR the NIC have been compared with individuals exposed to doses less than 0.01 Gy, and there is no demonstrable difference[45]. If the control group (both NIC and those less than 0.01 Gy) is removed from the analysis, the remaining data appear to show high consistency with a linear dose–response model; some analyses of this type were performed by Schull *et al*[38].

36   It can therefore be concluded that whilst there are no significant differences between mean IQ in the controls and either the 0.01–0.09 Gy or 0.10–0.49 Gy group, the data excluding those with SMR are consistent with a linear no-threshold model. Whilst the data are not inconsistent with a threshold in the region of 0.10 Gy (or possibly even 0.5 Gy, although the evidence for this is weaker), there is a possibility that the inclusion of those not in city has affected the mean IQ for the control group; excluding the control group reduces yet further the evidence for a threshold above 0.1 Gy. Overall, the loss of IQ in the most sensitive 8–15 week period[33] is 21–29 points at 1 Gy.

37   If the dose response for SMR is also interpreted in terms of a linear pattern of response then again there will be no threshold. However, since IQ broadly follows a

normal distribution in the population for the majority of individuals, the IQ shift needed to cause SMR would require exposure to a substantial radiation dose. On the basis of a shift in IQ of about 30 points per Gy this would imply that for a dose of 10 mSv the shift in IQ would be only 0.3 points, which would not be detectable and even 100 mSv would give a barely detectable change in IQ (3 IQ points). It should be noted, however, that although a reasonable interpretation of the data on SMR is that it increases linearly with increasing dose, corresponding to a shift of about 30 IQ points per Sv, this assessment is based on a limited epidemiological database, and with at present only a very rudimentary knowledge of the effect of radiation on early cortical development. Mole[43] has pointed out that SMR is characterised in the case of a boy who had come to autopsy (dose >1 Gy) by brain lesions (heterotopia) which are visible. Such dosage might be caused by greater doses than those which lead to IQ loss alone. However, of the five cases that have been imaged using magnetic resonance (MRI), two cases with heterotopia (very similar to that noted in the autopsied boy) have been seen and both received doses of less than 1 Gy (about 0.7 Gy). One further boy showed no evidence of visible abnormality on the MRI although he had a small head. His mother's estimated uterine dose[46] was 1.46 Gy. There is a clear need for further studies to examine the effect of radiation on the developing brain.

38 When exposures occur in the 16–25 week period the DS86 dosimetry suggests a threshold for SMR in the range 0.64–0.70 Gy with a lower 95% bound of 0.21 Gy. Thus, the risk at 1 Gy is about a quarter of that following exposure in the most sensitive 8–15 week period[37]. The difference in observed effect between this period and the more sensitive 8–15 week period is broadly consistent with the phases of brain development with a transitional period in which the neuronal cells are migrating and perhaps in a critical period of differentiation, and a later period when the neuronal cells are perhaps completing this transition[32].

39 At less than 8 weeks neither an increase in SMR nor a decrease in IQ is observed. This may be due to the lack of survival in any case in which damage is of sufficient severity to cause an effect. Indeed there is a deficiency in the number of people exposed at under 4 weeks gestational age amongst the atomic bomb survivors[37]. Alternatively it may be because the neurons that lead to formation of the cerebrum are not yet susceptible to developmental impairment by radiation damage, or because they are more easily replaced. There is also no evidence of SMR or IQ loss in cases exposed at greater than 25 weeks post-conception. This may be due to terminally differentiating cells becoming more radio-resistant or the increasing capacity of cortical tissue to sustain neuronal losses.

Dose and dose rate effects

40 Little is known about the effects of dose rate and dose fractionation on the response of the developing brain to prenatal irradiation. The data available have been reviewed by Konermann[35]. Most studies indicate that dose fractionation or protraction results in reduced developmental effects. It is reasonable to assume on the basis of the limited data available that radiation damage caused to the brain by ionising radiation has the potential for repair if the dose is fractionated or protracted and that estimates of risk based on exposures at high doses and high dose rates will, if anything, be likely to overestimate risks at low dose rates.

Conclusions

41   The series of studies on the atomic bomb survivors related to the effects of radiation on the developing brain all parallel each other and are reasonably consistent in suggesting the period of greatest *in utero* sensitivity is between 8 and 15 weeks of gestation, with a lower risk between 16 and 25 weeks, and no evidence of effects in the 0–8 week period or at times later than 25 weeks. There is good evidence for a threshold in response in the 16–25 week period but the evidence for a threshold in the 8–15 week period is equivocal. For the present it is assumed that the response increases with dose, with no threshold. The data on severe mental retardation and loss of IQ are in reasonable accord and are consistent with the interpretation that there is a dose-related shift in IQ of about 30 points per Gy (low LET).

RISKS OF CANCER

42   Information on the risk of cancer following irradiation *in utero* has been reviewed by UNSCEAR[2,30,47] and by the BEIR III and BEIR V Committees[6,8]. Current risk estimates for radiation-induced childhood cancer are based mainly on data collected in the Oxford Survey of Childhood Cancers (OSCC) concerning obstetric radiography. Information is also available from other studies of prenatal X-ray exposure that have been performed in the USA and elsewhere, and from the study of those irradiated *in utero* as a result of the atomic bombings of Hiroshima and Nagasaki.

Oxford Survey of Childhood Cancers (OSCC)

43   The Oxford Survey of Childhood Cancers is a continuing case–control study of childhood cancer deaths under 16 years of age in Great Britain. It was started in 1955 and now includes deaths during the period 1953–1979. During the late 1950s it was reported that a doubling in the risk of childhood cancer was associated with exposure to prenatal X-rays[48,49]. Later analyses covering a longer period indicated a falling risk with calendar time and yielded an average 40%–50% increase in childhood cancer associated with prenatal X-rays[50,51]. The magnitude of this increase was, in relative terms, similar for leukaemia and for solid tumours. According to Knox *et al*[52], the relative cancer risk was greatest at ages 4–7 years and appeared to tail off at higher ages within the range of ages considered (up to 15 years).

44   When the above findings were first published, there was concern regarding the interpretation of the study. It was suggested that, owing to the retrospective nature of OSCC, with at least partial reliance upon mothers' memories, some bias may have been introduced. The results of the follow-up were supported by an American study performed by MacMahon[53] based on contemporary records of X-ray exposure; an association between prenatal X-rays and childhood cancer was confirmed. The possibility still exists that there may be some as yet unidentified confounding factor affecting both the probability of the fetus being irradiated *in utero* and the risk of subsequent cancer. The data obtained by the Oxford survey were reanalysed, however, by Mole[54] who showed that the frequency of leukaemia and of solid cancers in childhood is greater following antenatal X-radiography not only in singleton births but also in dizygotic twins. The radiography rate was 10% in singletons and 55% in twins. A similar excess frequency of leukaemia and of solid cancers in those X-rayed with such different rates of radiography is strong evidence for irradiation as the cause.

45   The effect of other possible confounding factors such as sibship position, maternal age and social class was considered by Bithell and Stewart[51] and by Kneale and Stewart[55]. Generally the relative risk associated with prenatal X-rays was changed little after allowing for these factors. However, claims were made[56] that maternal illnesses may have affected both the probability of a prenatal X-ray examination being performed and the risk of cancer in the child subsequently. Consequently, Knox *et al*[52] undertook a further analysis of the OSCC data in which allowance was made simultaneously for illnesses and drugs administered to the mother during pregnancy, as well as for socio-demographic factors of the type mentioned above. It was claimed by Knox *et al* that these illnesses and drugs had masked rather than exaggerated the cancer risks associated with prenatal X-rays, and that the estimate of relative risk was increased from a value of around 1.4 obtained in earlier analyses to 1.94 when allowance was made for the illnesses and drugs. However, it was later determined that the difference between these values was due primarily to differences in the reference dates of births; the former value related to births averaged over the whole study, whereas the latter value related to those born in 1950, for whom the doses from prenatal X-rays were higher than in later years. The authors now acknowledge that illnesses and drugs in pregnancy do not confound the relative risk associated with prenatal X-rays and the relative risk calculated previously (1.4) remains appropriate[57].

46   Bithell and Stewart[51] found that the following factors modified the X-ray related risk: calendar period, number of films used in the examination, and trimester of irradiation. As regards the number of films, a linear relationship between this variable and the relative risk was demonstrated by Bithell and Stewart. However, in a recent analysis, Gilman *et al*[58] found that this relationship disappeared after allowing for the joint effects of trimester of irradiation and factors such as maternal age. Bithell[59] suggested that this may have been due to controlling for a factor such as maternal age that was strongly correlated with the number of films; the effect of adjusting for this factor would be to weaken the film–response relationship. Finally, Bithell and Stewart[51] indicated that the X-ray related risk for those exposed in the first trimester was higher than that for those exposed in the second or third trimesters: after allowing for factors such as the number of films, Gilman *et al*[58] estimated the ratio of risks as 2.7. However, those exposed in the second or third trimesters mostly received X-rays as part of an obstetric examination, whereas the small number of first trimester exposures mainly arose from non-obstetric examinations. About 25% of the latter type of examination involved fluoroscopy; furthermore non-obstetric X-ray examinations were markedly more frequent in future cases than controls only in the earliest years of the study, when resulting doses were likely to have been higher than in later years (see paragraph 54). Thus difference in fetal doses may account for the apparent variation in risks between trimesters[60]. It is concluded that there is insufficient reason to assume a higher risk of radiation-induced cancer in the first trimester than later in pregnancy.

Other studies in the UK and USA

47   A list of the largest studies on prenatal X-rays and childhood cancer is given by Bithell[59], based on a literature review by Rose[28]. If the studies are ranked by their statistical 'information content', corresponding to the precision of their risk estimate,

OSCC contains by far the most information (73%) of the 13 studies considered. Based on this measure, the next most informative study is that of MacMahon[53] – extended by Monson and MacMahon[61] – of childhood cancer in the north-eastern USA. Although of a case–control and, hence, retrospective nature, this study had the advantage mentioned earlier of being based on contemporary records of prenatal X-ray examinations; hence it avoided the possibility of recall bias in the assessment of exposure. MacMahon[53] determined a 40% excess of both leukaemia and other cancers among those irradiated *in utero*. However, the extension of the study[61] only showed a significant excess for leukaemia, which was confined to the first 8 years of life.

48   Other case–control studies yield estimates for the relative cancer risk associated with prenatal X-rays that are greater than unity[59]. These include a study of childhood cancer incidence in parts of England during the early 1980s[62,63] and, following the line developed by Mole[54] in attempting to reduce any selection bias, a study of twins in Connecticut[64]. It is interesting to note that the largest cohort study of prenatal X-rays and childhood cancer, namely that by Court Brown *et al*[65] of 40 000 UK children, did not show an excess risk. However, Bithell[54] pointed out that because of the low incidence of childhood cancer even a cohort study of this size lacked sufficient statistical power to identify an excess if the underlying relative risk was about 1.4; generally, case–control studies are of greater use in detecting excesses in risk when the baseline risk is small. Overall, Bithell[59] showed that the relative risks obtained from different studies are consistent, even though they relate to different populations and the studies sometimes differ in their design and method of analysis. With OSCC excluded, the weighted average of the relative risks is 1.36 (95% confidence limits, 1.20–1.51), which is significantly greater than unity and is consistent with the estimate of 1.4 obtained from OSCC. Inclusion of the OSCC estimate yields an average relative risk of 1.39 (95% confidence limits, 1.31–1.47).

Japanese atomic bomb survivors

49   The remaining major study of cancer following irradiation *in utero* concerns those exposed as a result of the atomic bombings of Hiroshima and Nagasaki. Jablon and Kato[66] examined cancer mortality up to age 10 years among 1250 children exposed to less than 5 Gy (based on the T65DR system). No excess in cancer mortality was observed – only one death occurred – whereas about five excess cancer deaths would have been expected on the basis of the OSCC risk estimates given by Stewart and Kneale[50]. However, in the further follow-up of this population[67] with a longer period of observation (1950–84), cancer incidence data as well mortality, a larger sample size (including cases ascertained by means additional to birth registrations) and use of the revised dosimetry system (DS86), 2 cases of childhood cancer were observed in individuals aged less than 15 years and 16 other cases of adult-type cancer (including 2 cases of leukaemia) were reported. While the number of observed cases (cancer of breast and uterus) roughly equalled that expected in the zero dose group, the relative risks in the three dose categories were 1.24, 2.18 and 4.78, with a statistically significant trend in relative risk with increasing dose ($p = 0.03$). Thus the data from the Japanese survivors can no longer be taken as evidence that the cancer increases seen in OSCC, and similar studies, were not causally related to *in utero* irradiation. It is of interest that there is no significant difference in the risk of cancer from exposure during different periods of gestation.

50   These Japanese data give an estimated relative risk at 1 Gy, for *in utero* irradiation, namely 3.77, that is similar to that observed to date among survivors irradiated in the first 10 years of life. However, it should be emphasised that the number of cancer cases among those irradiated *in utero* is small and the uncertainty, both in the value of the above relative risk (95% confidence interval 1.14–13.48)[68] and in the pattern of any future risk, is large. For more recent years (1985–89) there is no evidence of excess cancer risk[69]. But while it is unlikely that any large excess of leukaemia will now appear, the question of solid cancer risks following *in utero* exposure requires further follow-up.

51   There is some discrepancy between the results of *in utero* irradiation related to obstetric procedures and that related to the Japanese atomic bombings. In the former, leukaemia is an early effect and its occurrence reflects the usual overall pattern of childhood cancers, whereas the predominant effect in the Japanese survivors exposed *in utero* is an increased incidence of adult types of cancer.

52   It should be noted that there may be under-ascertainment for the earlier years of the Japanese study. The fact that follow-up of Japanese children exposed *in utero* is incomplete before 1950, makes direct comparison with OSCC results difficult, since in the latter study the relative risk declines markedly after 4–7 years.

53   Some animal data provide evidence of a carcinogenic effect from *in utero* irradiation. An enhanced sensitivity to postnatal exposures to carcinogens was found by Nomura[70]; this would be compatible with an increase in cancers in adult life. Morin *et al*[71] have demonstrated that the lifetime tumour risk in rats varied with age at irradiation; it decreased by about ten-fold in rats irradiated at 9 months compared with rats irradiated *in utero*; in the latter group there were slightly more tumours (largely of central nervous system and gonads) than in the group irradiated at 3 months. The mechanism for this sensitivity, as well as for that suggested by the OSCC data, has yet to be determined.

Risk estimates

54   OSCC provides the largest body of data on the effects in childhood of *in utero* irradiation. In deriving risk estimates from these data, there has been considerable uncertainty about the fetal dose. Bithell and Stiller[72] estimated the excess number of fatal cancer cases up to age 15 years following irradiation, in the third trimester, as approximately 4.5% Gy^{-1}, based on the UNSCEAR estimates[47] of 'average fetal dose per obstetric X-ray film', decreasing from 18 mGy in 1943–49 to 2 mGy in 1960–65. Mole[42] has pointed to the unreliability of this dose estimation procedure, and has used instead the Adrian Committee's measurement of skin dose to the mother during obstetric X-ray procedures in the third trimester of pregnancy, in 1958, as the basis for assessing fetal dose for cases exposed in 1958–61 (approximately 6 mGy)[73]. This results in a very similar risk estimate for cancer induction (at this time mortality reflected incidence) up to the age of 15 years of 4% –5% Gy^{-1}. Muirhead and Kneale's analysis[57] of the extended OSCC database (up to 1979), including *in utero* exposures in all trimesters of pregnancy and non-fatal as well as fatal cancers, in children up to 14 years of age, was based on the UNSCEAR estimates of dose per obstetric X-ray film. The resulting risk estimate is 6.4% Gy^{-1}.

55   However, to allow for uncertainties in the mean fetal doses for OSCC in particular, as well as in the length of expression of the risk and in between-trimester risks, the number of excess cancer cases following irradiation *in utero*, to age 15 years, will be taken as 6 10^{-2} Gy^{-1} (low LET). This is the same as the BEIR III[8] value, but for incident cases rather than deaths. Since slightly less than 50% of childhood cancers consist of leukaemia and other lymphatic/haemopoietic cancers[74], and the relative risks are similar for these and other cancers, a risk of 2.5 10^{-2} Gy^{-1} will be assumed for leukaemia and 3.5 10^{-2} Gy^{-1} for solid cancers. Also, as slightly less than half of all childhood cancers are fatal[74] the number of excess cancer deaths will be taken as 3 10^{-2} Gy^{-1}, comprising 1.25 10^{-2} Gy^{-1} for leukaemias and 1.75 10^{-2} Gy^{-1} for solid cancers (Table 6.2). To this risk of fatal childhood cancer must be added that occurring later in life (> 15 years). Obviously the lifetime cancer risk is influenced largely by the risk of solid cancers occurring in adult life. Since the types of adult cancer differ from those arising in childhood (which are mainly leukaemias and tumours of the central nervous system) it is more appropriate to use data from the Japanese atomic bomb survivors, on adult cancers following *in utero* exposure, rather than the childhood data, in attempting to project risks over a lifetime. Based on the similarity in risks of adult cancers among atomic bomb survivors irradiated *in utero* and those exposed at ages 0–9 years[67] the overall risk of fatal cancer following exposure *in utero* may exceed that in the first 15 years of life by a factor up to four (Table 6.3). However, there are considerable uncertainties in projecting lifetime risks from the current data, and the overall risk may be lower, perhaps of the order of twice that in the first 15 years of life. The risk estimates up to age 15 years are therefore considered to be the more reliable.

Conclusions

56   The risk coefficients developed above are derived from follow-up studies on children irradiated *in utero* with maximum doses in the range 10–20 mGy (low LET), depending on the calendar period (see paragraph 54). They are therefore directly applicable for estimating risks of low doses and low dose rates (see Chapter 8).

57   The fatal cancer risk up to age 15 years, resulting from *in utero* irradiation is 3 10^{-2} Gy^{-1} comprising 1.25 10^{-2} Gy^{-1} for leukaemia and 1.75 10^{-2} Gy^{-1} for solid cancers. The total incidence of leukaemia and solid cancer is taken to be twice that for fatality, giving an overall risk of cancer of 6 10^{-2} Gy^{-1} (Table 6.2). With the current uncertainties in projecting lifetime risks of fatal cancer following *in utero* exposure, the risks up to 15 years provide a firmer basis at present for risk assessment and practical management in radiological protection. Comparison can be made with a natural cumulative risk of fatal cancer up to the age of 15 years, in the UK, of 1 in 1300 (7.7 10^{-4}).

Cancer following exposure in early gestation

58   Clearly, there can be no risk during the first 10 days of the menstrual cycle since no conception can have occurred but the interval prior to pregnancy declaration will also

Cancer type	Fatal	Non-fatal	Total
Leukaemia	1.25	1.25	2.5
Others	1.75	1.75	3.5
Total	3	3	6

TABLE 6.2
Risk of cancer up to age 15 years, following in utero exposure (10^{-2} Sv^{-1})

Note Based on UK national rates. The baseline cancer incidence in the first 15 years of life is about *1 in 650*, ie approximately *1.5 10^{-3}* (OPCS[74]). About half of these cancers are fatal.

TABLE 6.3
Stochastic effects
following low LET
irradiation of the
human embryo

Exposure age	Fatal cancer risks (10^{-2} Sv^{-1})		
	Time since exposure (y)		
	< 15	< 40	Lifetime projection
In utero	3	—	~11[a]
0–9 years	~0.6[c]	~1.2[b]	~11[b]

Notes
(a) Based on the similarity of risk of adult cancers among atomic bomb survivors irradiated *in utero* and those exposed at ages 0–9 years (Yoshimoto *et al*[67]).
(b) As given in Table 4.7 for low dose rate.
(c) The risk up to 15 years following exposure is about half of that up to 40 years after exposure and, based on the models developed in Chapter 4, comprises largely the risk of leukaemia[27]. This leukaemia risk is about half of that for the first 15 years of life following *in utero* exposure. However, the main determinant of the lifetime risk, both for *in utero* exposure and exposure at ages 0–9 years, is the risk of solid cancers in adulthood (see paragraph 55).

encompass the 2–3 week phase of embryogenesis, possibly through to the onset of organogenesis at 4 weeks post-conception, ie around 6 weeks from the onset of the previous menstruation.

59   Implicit in current ICRP recommendations[75] is that there is no cancer risk following irradiation within the first 3 weeks following conception. Although not specifically stated, this view probably derives from the earlier belief that radiation damage in these early phases of embryogenesis will result in cell death which, unless it results in termination of embryonic development, will have no biological consequences. By restricting the biological consequences of early *in utero* irradiation to cell killing the possibility of cancer induction may be discounted but this ignores any consequences deriving from the induction of somatic mutation in early pluripotent or multipotential embryonic stem cells. The possibility of such radiation-induced mutant cells contributing to embryonic mal-development and cancer has been suggested by Gaulden and Murry[22].

60   During the 3 week post-conception period the zygote will have completed the early cell cleavage processes and made the transition from the morula stage to the implanted blastocyst. The total number of target embryonic cells for the induction of a cancer-associated mutational event will be small relative to the number present during later phases of organogenesis but there is a certain probability, albeit low, that irradiation could result in the induction of a cancer-initiating mutation in a single embryonic cell. While it remains likely that many such mutations will result in gross developmental abnormality and consequent embryonic/fetal loss there is evidence that some cancer-associated mutations of this type do not result in such losses nor indeed lead to recognisable developmental abnormalities.

61   In particular, it is now apparent that some cancer-predisposing germ line mutations are dominantly inherited such that a mutation passed from either parent to the zygote is present in all developing somatic cells in the embryo. This mutation does not lead to embryonic/fetal loss or to congenital malformation but, instead, predisposes the live-born to spontaneously arising cancer[76]. For some mutations, eg those in retinoblastoma and Wilms tumour genes, the resulting cancers arise in childhood and are relatively organ specific; for others, eg *p53* gene mutations, cancer susceptibility is not so clearly organ specific and may be expressed in later life[77,78]. These observations serve to make the point that cancer-associated mutation in early somatic cells of the embryo is, in some circumstances, compatible with 'normal' development. Thus, although no direct evidence is available, it is reasonable to suppose that propagation of a somatically acquired mutation of this type through early *in utero* irradiation could lead to cancer in the offspring.

62   The relatively small number of target embryonic cells present during the 3 week post-conception period and the small number of known genes that could mediate such effects would argue that the cancer risk will be very low. Conversely, however, the early induction of such rare somatic cell events will tend to result in a major contribution of that mutant cell to somatic tissues of the offspring and, as in the case of some heritable mutations of this type, an increase in the probability of cancer development. Thus, although it is possible that the risk of radiation-induced cancer following irradiation during the 3 week post-conception period will be much lower than that pertaining to later phases of fetogenesis there is reason to believe that the cancer risk is not zero.

HEREDITARY EFFECTS

63   Hereditary effects are discussed in Chapter 5. Genetic studies in offspring of atomic bomb survivors have not shown any significant radiation-related increases in any measure of genetic damage employed. In experiments in mice the sensitivity of fetal gonads was comparable to that of adult gonads or a little lower[1]. It is therefore assumed here that the risks from *in utero* irradiation are the same as after birth, 2.4×10^{-2} Sv^{-1} following exposure of either male or female germ cells[2]. It may be that this will be lower in early embryogenesis and fetogenesis prior to the establishment of germinal tissues.

CONCLUSIONS

64   On the basis of the mechanisms involved and the results of animal studies, it is likely that radiation-induced malformations in humans, following exposures *in utero*, have an acute dose threshold – possibly 0.25 to 2 Gy, which may be further increased by protraction of dose. The risk of malformations being induced by *in utero* exposure to low doses of radiation at low dose rates is very small in comparison with normal, spontaneously arising risks.

65   A series of studies on the atomic bomb survivors related to the effects of radiation on the developing brain all parallel each other and are reasonably consistent in suggesting the period of greatest *in utero* sensitivity is between 8 and 15 weeks of gestation, with a lower risk between 16 and 25 weeks, and no evidence of effects in the 0–8 week period or at times later than 25 weeks. There is good evidence for a threshold in response in the 16–25 week period but the evidence for a threshold in the 8–15 week period is equivocal. For the present it is assumed that for exposures between 8 and 15 weeks the response increases with dose, without threshold. The data on severe

mental retardation and loss of IQ are in reasonable accord and are consistent with the interpretation that there is a dose-related shift in IQ of about 30 points per Gy (low LET).

66   Estimates of cancer risk to age 15 years have been obtained by combining the excess risk observed in the Oxford Survey of Childhood Cancer with estimates of dose to the fetus from obstetric X-rays. This yields an estimated risk of leukaemia of 2.5×10^{-2} Gy^{-1} and of other cancers of 3.5×10^{-2} Gy^{-1} (low LET); about half of these cases are assumed to be fatal. These risk coefficients for cancer are directly applicable to low doses and low dose rates. The lifetime risk of fatal cancer following exposure *in utero* may exceed that in the first 15 years of life by a factor up to four. There are, however, considerable uncertainties in projecting lifetime risks from the current date and this factor may perhaps be about two.

67   For hereditary risks it is assumed that the risks from *in utero* exposure are the same as after birth, 2.4×10^{-2} Sv^{-1} following irradiation of male or female germ cells.

REFERENCES

1   Searle, A G. Mutation induction in mice. *Adv. Radiat. Biol.*, **4**, 121–207 (1974).

2   UNSCEAR. Genetic and somatic effects of ionising radiation. Report to the General Assembly, with annexes. Annex A: Genetic effects of radiation and Annex C: Biological effects of pre-natal irradiation. New York, United Nations (1986).

3   Brent, R L, and Harris, M. The prevention of embryonic, fetal and perinatal disease. Washington DC, US Government Printing Office (1976).

4   Brent, R L, Beckman, D A, and Jensh, R P. Relative radiosensitivity of fetal tissue. *Adv. Radiat. Biol.*, **12**, 239 (1987).

5   Müller, W U, and Streffer, C. Lethal and teratogenic effects after exposure to x-rays at various times of early murine gestation. *Teratology*, **42**, 643–50 (1990).

6   BEIR V. Health effects of exposure to low levels of ionising radiation. Washington DC, NAS/NRC (1990).

7   Rugh, R, *et al.* Persistent stunting following x-irradiation of the fetus. *Am. J. Anat.*, **115**, 185–198 (1964).

8   BEIR III. The effects on populations of exposure to low levels of ionising radiation. Washington DC, NAS/NRC (1980).

9   Mole, R H. Irradiation of the embryo and fetus. *Br. J. Radiol.*, **60**, 17–31 (1987).

10   Brent, R L. Radiation teratogenesis. *Teratology*, **21**, 281–98 (1980).

11   Mole, R H. Expectation of malformations after irradiation of the developing human *in utero*: the experimental basis for predictions. *Adv. Radiat. Biol.*, **15**, 217–301 (1992).

12   Russell, W L. Genetic effects of radiation in mammals. IN: *Radiation Biology*, Part II. New York, McGraw-Hill (1954).

13   Stather, J W, Muirhead, C R, Edwards, A A, Harrison, J D, Lloyd, D C, and Wood, N R. Health effects models developed from the 1988 UNSCEAR report. Chilton, NRPB-R226 (1988) (London, HMSO).

14   Brent, R L, and Bolden, B T. The indirect effect of irradiation on embryonic development. III. The contribution of ovarian irradiation, uterine irradiation, oviduct irradiation and zygote irradiation to fetal mortality and growth retardation in the rat. *Radiat. Res.*, **14**, 453 (1967).

15   Russell, L B, Badgett, A K, and Saylors, C L. Comparison of the effects of acute, continuous and fractionated irradiation during embryonic development. IN: *Immediate and Low-level Effects of Ionising Radiation.*. Proceedings of Conference, Venice. London, Taylor and Francis (1960).

16   Müller, W U, Streffer, C, and Pampfer, S. Teratogenic effects of ionizing radiation after exposure of pre-implantation stages of mouse embryos. IN: *Low Dose Radiation: Biological Bases of Risk Assessment* (Eds K F Baverstock and J W Stather). London, Taylor and Francis, pp 677–81 (1989).

17   Pamfer, S, and Streffer, C. Prenatal death and malformations after irradiation of mouse zygotes with neutrons or x-rays. *Teratology*, **37**, 599–607 (1988).

18   Friedberg, W, Hannemann, G D, Faulkner, D N, Darden, E B, and Neal, R B. Prenatal survival of mice irradiated with fission neutrons or 300 kVp x-rays during the pronuclear-zygote stage: survival curves, effect of dose fractionation. *Int. J. Radiat. Biol.*, **24**, 549–60 (1973).

19   Schlesinger, D M, and Brent, R L. Effects of x-irradiation during preimplantation stages of gestation on cell viability and embryo survival in the mouse. *Radiat. Res.,* **75**, 202–16 (1978).

20   Roux, C, Horvath, C, and Dupuis R. Effects of preimplantation low-dose radiation on rat embryos. *Health Phys.,* **45**, 993–9 (1983).

21   Pampfer, S, and Streffer, C. Increased chromosome aberration levels in cells from mouse fetuses after zygote x-irradiation. *Int. J. Radiat. Biol.,* **55**, No. 1, 85–92 (1989).

22   Gaulden, M E, and Murry, R C. Medical radiation and possible adverse effects on the human embryo. IN *Radiation Biology in Cancer Research* (Eds R E Meyn and H R Withers). New York, Raven Press, pp 277–94 (1980).

23   Yamazaki, J N, et al. Outcome of pregnancy in women exposed to the atomic bomb in Nagasaki. *Am. J. Dis. Children,* **87**, 448–63 (1954).

24   Wood, J W, et al. The growth and development of children exposed in utero to the atomic bombs in Hiroshima and Nagasaki. *Am. J. Pub. Health,* **57**, 1374–80 (1967).

25   Yamazaki, J N, and Schull, W J. Perinatal loss and neurological abnormalities among children of the atomic bomb: Nagasaki and Hiroshima re-visited, 1949–1989. *JAMA,* **264**, 605–9 (1990).

26   Miller, R W. Effects of pre-natal exposure to ionising radiation. *Health Phys.,* **59**, 57–61 (1990).

27   Muirhead, C R. Personal Communication (1992).

28   Rose, K S B. Epidemiological surveys of the effects of low-level radiation dose: A comparative assessment. Harwell, UKAEA, AERE-R12045, Volume B Intra-uterine irradiation effects (1990).

29   Nokkentved, K. Effect of diagnostic radiation on the human fetus. Copenhagen, Verlag Munksgaard (1968).

30   UNSCEAR. Sources and effects of ionising radiation. Report to the General Assembly, with annexes. New York, United Nations (1977).

31   Burrow, G N, et al. Study of adolescents exposed *in utero* to the atomic bombs. Nagasaki, Japan. *JAMA,* **192**, 357–64 (1965).

32   ICRP. Developmental effects of irradiation on the brain of the embryo and fetus. ICRP Publication 49. *Ann. ICRP,* **16**, No. 4, 1–43 (1986).

33   Schull, W J. Ionising radiation and the developing human brain. IN: Risks associated with ionising radiations. *Ann. ICRP,* **22**, No. 1, 95–118 (1991).

34   Beebe, G W, and Usagawa, M. The major ABCC samples. Hiroshima, Atomic Bomb Casualty Commission TR12-68 (1968).

35   Konermann, G. Post implantation development following ionizing irradiation. *Adv. Radiat. Biol.,* **13**, 91–167 (1987).

36   Wood, J W, Johnson, K G, and Omori, Y. *In utero* exposure to the Hiroshima atomic bomb: Follow-up at twenty years. Hiroshima, Atomic Bomb Casualty Commission, TR9-65 (1965).

37   Otake, M, Yoshimaru, H, and Schull, W J. Severe mental retardation among the prenatally exposed survivors of the atomic bombing of Hiroshima and Nagasaki: A comparison of the T65DR and DS86 dosimetry systems. Hiroshima, Radiation Effects Research Foundation, TR16–87 (1987).

38   Schull, W J, Otake, M, and Yoshimaru, H. Effect on intelligence test score of prenatal exposure to ionizing radiation in Hiroshima and Nagasaki: A comparison of the T65DR and DS86 dosimetry systems. Hiroshima, Radiation Effects Research Foundation, TR3-88 (1988).

39   Otake, M, Schull, W J, Fujikoshi, Y, and Yoshimaru, H. Effect on school performance of prenatal exposure to ionizing radiation in Hiroshima: A comparison of the T65DR and DS86 dosimetry systems. Hiroshima, Radiation Effects Research Foundation, TR2-88 (1988).

40   Dunn, K, Yoshimaru, H, Otake, M, Annegers, J F, and Schull, W J. Prenatal exposure to ionizing radiation and subsequent development of seizures. *Am. J. Epidemiol.,* **131**, 114–23 (1990).

41   Otake, M, Schull, W J, and Yoshimaru, H. A review of radiation-related brain damage in the prenatally exposed atomic bomb survivors. Hiroshima, Radiation Effects Research Foundation, Report TR4-89 (1990).

42   Mole, R H. Fetal dosimetry by UNSCEAR and risk coefficients for childhood cancer following diagnostic radiology in pregnancy. *J. Radiol. Prot.,* **10**, 199–203 (1990).

43   Mole, R H. The effect of prenatal radiation exposure on the developing human brain. *Int. J. Radiat. Biol.,* **57**, 647–63 (1990).

44   Mole, R H. Severe mental retardation after large prenatal exposures to bomb radiation. Reduction in oxygen transport to fetal brain: A possible abscopal mechanism. *Int. J. Radiat. Biol.*, **58**, 705–711 (1990).

45   Schull, W J. Personal communication (1992).

46   Schull, W J, Nishitami, H, Hasuo, K, *et al.* Brain aberrations among the mentally retarded prenatally exposed survivors of the atomic bombings of Hiroshima and Nagasaki. Hiroshima, Radiation Effects Research Foundation, TR13-91 (1991).

47   UNSCEAR. Ionising radiation: Levels and effects. Report to the General Assembly, with annexes. Volume II: Effects. New York, United Nations (1972).

48   Stewart, A M, Webb, J W, Giles, B D, and Hewitt, D. Malignant disease in childhood and diagnostic irradiation *in utero*. *Lancet*, **2**, 447 (1956).

49   Stewart, A M, Webb, J W, and Hewitt, D. A survey of childhood malignancies. *Br. Med. J.*, **1**, 1495 (1958).

50   Stewart, A M, and Kneale, G W. Radiation dose effects in relation to obstetric x-rays and childhood cancers. *Lancet*, **1**, 1185 (1970).

51   Bithell, J F, and Stewart, A M. Pre-natal irradiation and childhood malignancy: A review of British data from the Oxford Survey. *Br. J. Cancer*, **35**, 271 (1975).

52   Knox, E G, Stewart, A M, Kneale, G W, and Gilman, E A. Prenatal irradiation and childhood cancer. *J. Radiol. Prot.*, **7**, 177 (1987).

53   MacMahon, B. Prenatal x-ray exposure and childhood cancer. *J. Natl Cancer Inst.*, **28**, 1173 (1962).

54   Mole, R H. Antenatal irradiation and childhood cancer. Causation or coincidence. *Br. J. Cancer*, **30**, 199 (1974).

55   Kneale, G W, and Stewart, A M. Mantel-Haenszel analysis of Oxford data: II. Independent effects of fetal irradiation subfactors. *J. Natl Cancer Inst.*, **57**, 1009 (1976).

56   Totter, J R, and MacPherson, H G. Do childhood cancers result from prenatal x-rays? *Health Phys.*, **40**, 511 (1981).

57   Muirhead, C R, and Kneale, G W. Pre-natal irradiation and childhood cancer. *J. Radiol. Prot.*, **9**, 209–12 (1989).

58   Gilman, E A, Kneale, G W, Knox, E G, and Stewart, A M. Pregnancy x-rays and childhood cancers: Effects of exposure age and radiation dose. *J. Radiol. Prot.*, **8**, 3 (1988).

59   Bithell, J F. Epidemiological studies of children irradiated *in utero*. IN: *Low Dose Radiation: Biological Bases of Risk Assessment* (Eds K F Baverstock and J W Stather). London, Taylor and Francis, pp 77–87 (1989).

60   Mole, R H. Childhood cancer after prenatal exposure to diagnostic x-ray examinations in Britain. *Br. J. Cancer*, **62** 152–168 (1990).

61   Monson, R R, and MacMahon, B. Prenatal x-ray exposure and cancer in children. IN: *Radiation Carcinogenesis: Epidemiology and Biological Significance* (Eds J D Boice and J F Fraumeni). New York, Raven Press, p 97 (1984).

62   Hopton, P A, McKinney, P A, Cartwright, R A, *et al.* X-rays in pregnancy and the risk of childhood cancer. *Lancet*, **2**, 773 (1985).

63   McKinney, P A, Cartwright, R A, Saiu, J M T, *et al.* The inter-regional epidemiological study of childhood cancer (IRESCC): A case-control study of aetiological factors in leukaemia and lymphoma. *Arch. Disease Childhood*, **62**, 279–87 (1987).

64   Harvey, E B, Boice, J D, Honeyman, M, and Flannery, J T. Prenatal x-ray exposure and childhood cancer in twins. *New. Engl. J. Med.*, **312**, 541 (1985).

65   Court Brown, W M, Doll, R, and Hill, A B. Incidence of leukaemia after exposure to diagnostic radiation *in utero*. *Br. Med. J.*, **2**, 1539 (1960).

66   Jablon, S, and Kato, H. Childhood cancer in relation to prenatal exposure to atomic bomb radiation. *Lancet*, **2**, 1000 (1970).

67   Yoshimoto, Y, Kato, H, and Schull, W J. Risk of cancer among children exposed *in utero* to A-bomb radiations, 1950–84. *Lancet*, **2**, 665 (1988).

68   Kato, H, *et al.* Risk of cancer among children exposed to atomic bomb radiation *in utero*. A review. IN: *Perinatal and Multigeneration Carcinogenesis*. Lyon, International Agency for Research on Cancer (1989).

69   Yoshimoto, Y, Soda, M, and Mabuchi, K. Health risks of atomic bomb survivors: the experience of those exposed *in utero* or early in childhood. IN: *International Conference on Radiation Effects and Protection*. Mito, Ibavaki, Japan, JAERI, pp 80–85 (1992).

70   Nomura, T. Role of radiation-induced mutations in multigeneration carcinogenesis. IN: *Perinatal and Multigeneration Carcinogenesis.* Lyon, International Agency for Research on Cancer (1989).

71   Morin, M, Masse, R, and Lafuma J. The effect of age at irradiation on tumour development. *C R Acad. Sci. Paris,* **312**, (III), 629–34 (1991).

72   Bithell, J F, and Stiller, C A. The carcinogenic risk of obstetric x-raying. Oxford, University of Oxford, Department of Statistics, Technical Report No. JFB-TR1 (1988).

73   Adrian, Lord. Radiological hazards to patients; second report of the Committee under Lord Adrian. London, HMSO (1960).

74   OPCS. Cancer statistics: Incidence, survival and mortality in England and Wales. Studies on Medical and Population Subjects, No. 43. London, HMSO (1981).

75   ICRP. 1990 Recommendations of the International Commission on Radiological Protection. ICRP Publication 60. *Ann. ICRP,* **21**, Nos 1–3 (1991).

76   Knudson, A G. Genetics of human cancer. *Ann. Rev. Genet.,* **20**, 231 (1986).

77   Sagar, R. Tumour suppressor genes: The puzzle and the promise. *Science,* **246**, 1406–1412 (1989).

78   Weinberg, R A. Tumour suppressor genes. *Science,* **254**, 1138–1146 (1991).

7 Relative Biological Effectiveness

INTRODUCTION

1   There are extensive radiobiological data which indicate that high LET radiations (neutrons and alpha particles) have a greater biological effect than low LET radiation. The influence of radiation quality on a specified biological system is usually quantified in terms of its relative biological effectiveness (RBE). The RBE of a specific radiation can be defined as:

$$RBE = \frac{\text{Dose of reference radiation required to produce a specific level of response}}{\text{Dose of radiation } A \text{ required to produce an equal response}}$$

with all physical and biological variables, except radiation quality, being held constant, as far as is possible. This definition does not depend on the dose response for the two radiations being the same, it simply depends on comparing the dose to give a specific level of effect for a particular endpoint. It is usual to use low LET radiation (X-rays or gamma rays) as the reference radiation. A particular form of RBE is RBE_m which is the maximum RBE that would be obtained at low doses and low dose rates. Various authors and committees (eg Sinclair[1] and UNSCEAR[2]) have reviewed the relevant biological data. The latest review relevant to radiation quality is that from NCRP[3] which contains a comprehensive summary of the literature and re-analyses of the data to derive values for RBE_m.

2   It is apparent from these reviews that the RBE for high LET radiation is dependent on the biological response being studied. For early effects in tissues caused by cell killing (eg skin burns, cataracts and sterility) an ICRP task group[4] concluded that for a range of tissues and for both neutrons and alpha particles the RBE was generally less than 10. For damage to the lung from inhaled alpha particles causing fibrosis and loss of fluid into the lung (pneumonitis) the RBE for rats and beagle dogs was estimated to be in the range from about 7 to 10. Similarly, for the induction of chromosome aberrations in human blood lymphocytes by alpha particles from ^{242}Cm, RBE values of about 6 have been obtained in comparison with X-rays and 18 in comparison with gamma rays[5]. For the induction of micronuclei (caused by fragmentation of chromosomes) in lymphocytes by alpha particles from ^{239}Pu an RBE of 3.6 has been found at low doses (< 1 Gy)[6] and for DNA double strand breaks in Ehrlich ascites tumour cells (EATC) RBEs in the range 1.6–3.8 were found[7].

3   In a few experimental studies a biological effect has been obtained for alpha particle irradiation although a similar effect has not been found with low LET radiation. Studies in which sister chromatid exchanges (SCE) have been measured in human lymphocytes in the G_0 stage of the cell cycle give a measurable frequency of SCEs following exposure to alpha particles from ^{241}Am but no effect of X-ray irradiation was obtained. From the definition of RBE given above this implies an infinite RBE, although it is solely a consequence of the lack of effect of X-rays[8]. Similar results have been reported[9] for SCEs in Chinese hamster ovary cells irradiated in the G_1 phase of the cell cycle by ^{238}Pu alpha particles or X-rays. High values of RBE, up to about 245, have also

been reported[10] for sperm head abnormalities in mice when the effect of external exposure to X-rays was compared with the effects of tissue incorporated ^{241}Am. This may partly be accounted for by the heterogeneous distribution of ^{241}Am incorporated in the testis; it is known that actinides such as ^{241}Am tend to concentrate in interstitial tissue in the mouse testis, in close proximity to the developing sperm cells.

4   For tumour induction, a number of studies have demonstrated that both high and low LET radiation may induce cancer in a range of tissues. The available data relevant to the choice of RBEs for neutrons and alpha particles are summarised below.

NEUTRONS

5   Table 7.1 shows a summary of values for RBE_m obtained for various biological endpoints in mammals and mammalian cells for fission neutrons compared with gamma rays. Similar reviews have been published by UNSCEAR[11] and Sinclair[1]. Information on the variation of RBE_m with neutron energy comes partly from data from cellular studies, in particular using point mutations, chromosomal aberrations and cell transformation as endpoints.

Endpoint	RBE_m
Cytogenetic studies, human lymphocytes in culture	34–53
Cell transformation	3–80
Genetic endpoints in mammalian systems	5–70
Life shortening, mouse	10–46
Tumour induction	16–59

TABLE 7.1
Summary of estimated RBE_m values for fission neutrons versus gamma rays from NRCP[3]

6   There is uncertainty in the value for RBE_m for fission neutrons which lies principally in how the acute low LET data, mainly for cancer induction and life shortening in mammals, are extrapolated to low doses and low dose rates. These are the same data that form one of the bases for the judgement of dose and dose rate effectiveness factor (DDREF) (see Chapter 3). Thus the derivation of values for RBE_m and the low dose rate reduction factor are interrelated, which implies that the judgement factors, w_R (ICRP[12]) and DDREF, are interdependent.

7   The way this correlation can be taken into account is illustrated in Figure 7.1. The straight line A of slope α_H represents the dose–effect relationship for high LET radiation. The data points are representative of low LET acute data and can be extrapolated to low doses by the linear relationship B of slope α_{LH} or by curve C. Curve D represents the extrapolated linear portion slope α_{LL} of the low dose–response of curve C and is typical of dose–effect relationships for low LET exposure at low dose rates. The ratio of the slopes of curves A (slope α_H) and D (slope α_{LL}) represents RBE_m. The ratio of the slopes of curves B (slope α_{LH}) and D represents the DDREF. To avoid

FIGURE 7.1
*Typical dose-effect
relationships*

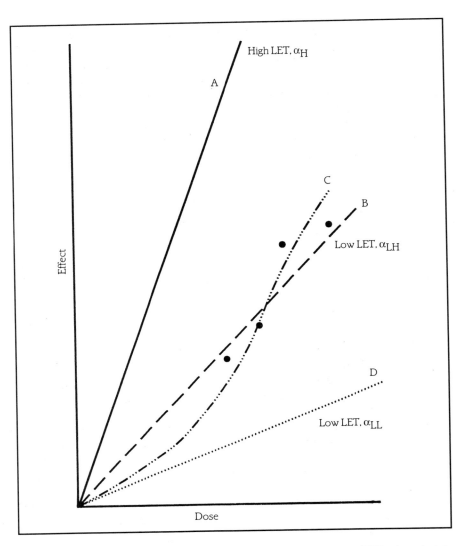

FIGURE 7.1 Typical dose-effect relationships

the non-linear extrapolation of low LET data involved in estimating RBE_m directly it is possible to estimate RBE_m from the ratio of the slopes of curves A and B and then multiply by the judged DDREF of 2 (see Chapter 3). When this technique is applied to animal data comparing fission neutrons and gamma rays, values for RBE_m generally lie in the range 5–20 rather than 10–60 as indicated in Table 7.1. For cellular data the extrapolation of acute low LET data to low doses is more certain than with animal studies so that RBE_m can be estimated directly.

8   There are few data in whole animals which measure the variation of RBE_m for specific tumour induction or life shortening (caused mainly by tumour induction, Chapter 3), with neutron energy. Knowledge of the variation of RBE_m with neutron energy is confined to cellular studies. Chromosomal aberrations in human lymphocytes[5,47] indicate a monotonic increase of about a factor of four from 14 MeV

down to 1 MeV. Mutations in a human hamster hybrid cell line (A_L) indicated[13] a monotonic decrease of about a factor of seven from 0.3 to 14 MeV. The oncogenic transformation of 10T½ cells showed a more erratic variation with neutron energy[14] but an overall variation of a factor of three from 230 keV to 14 MeV with a peak at 350 keV is indicated. The cellular data suggest a decrease in RBE_m of about a factor of four from 100 keV with increase of neutron energy. There is very little experimental data at lower neutron energies. Some cellular data observing chromosome aberrations in human lymphocytes[48] suggest an RBE_m close to that for fission neutrons whereas similar data from Sevankaev *et al*[15] suggest lower values.

9   ICRP[12] has established radiation weighting factors w_R for neutron exposure and has recommended that these are based on the incident radiation. Values are shown in Table 7.2 and it is seen that they reasonably take account of information on RBE_m except at low neutron energies. The rational basis for the reduction of w_R at lower neutron energies is that, in man, an increasing part of the absorbed dose due to neutrons is caused by gamma rays from neutron capture in hydrogen[16]. For neutron energies below 10 keV the gamma ray contribution ranges from 70% to nearly 100% of the dose, depending on the energy and the organ depth within the body, and this low LET component will have a value of $w_R = 1$. The reduced w_R values at low neutron energies are influenced by this component.

ALPHA PARTICLES

10   Alpha particles have a very short range in tissue. For the highest energy natural alpha particles from ^{226}Ra and its decay products with an energy range up to about 7.8 MeV the maximum range is about 80 μm; for 5 MeV alpha particles from ^{239}Pu the range is about 40 μm. These dimensions may be compared with the dimensions of the cell nucleus which range from about 5 to 10 μm diameter. The dose that a single alpha particle delivers crossing the cell nucleus, considered to be the radiosensitive target, is very variable. It may range from very low doses for particles which graze the nucleus,

Type and energy range	Radiation weighting factor w_R
Photons, all energies	1
Electrons and muons, all energies	1
Neutrons, energy < 10 keV	5
> 10 keV – 100 keV	10
> 100 keV – 2 MeV	20
> 2 MeV – 20 MeV	10
> 20 MeV	5
Protons, energy > 2 MeV	5
Alpha particles, fission fragments, heavy nuclei	20

TABLE 7.2
Radiation weighting factors recommended by ICRP[12]

to more than 1 Gy for particles crossing the diameter. Thus the concept of average tissue dose is a considerable simplification and individual cells in a tissue will receive very different doses. Furthermore, alpha emitting radionuclides may be deposited on the surfaces of organs within the body; this is the case for radon decay products deposited in the lung and for plutonium isotopes accumulated by the skeleton. There can therefore be a very heterogeneous distribution of alpha particle dose within an organ (or tissue). The specified dose depends on whether an average organ dose or the mean dose to a particular localised tissue volume is calculated. In practice it is usual to estimate average organ dose.

11   For an assessment of the appropriate RBE to use for estimating the risk of tumour induction in organs and tissues there are rather limited data available. The main difficulty is that comparable patterns of exposure are needed for both the alpha emitting and the reference radiation (X-rays or gamma rays). Although extensive data are available on tumour induction for either of these radiations on their own, their effects have been directly compared much less frequently. Published data relevant to the estimation of RBE_m are available for the induction of bone sarcomas and lung tumours in experimental animals, from studies on cells in culture and, to a limited extent, from epidemiological studies on human populations.

Experimental studies

Bone tumours in experimental animals

12   NCRP[3] reviewed experiments[17] on the induction of bone cancer in beagles injected with the alpha emitter ^{226}Ra and the beta emitter ^{90}Sr. Results were compared with similar experiments using mice[18,19]. There were strong similarities in the two experiments. In both, the incidence of bone sarcomas increased nearly linearly following ^{226}Ra injection up to doses of about 20 Gy while for ^{90}Sr there was a greater risk, per unit dose, at high doses than at low doses; the increase was superlinear. The greatest uncertainty in calculating RBE_m came from assumptions concerning the extrapolation of the ^{90}Sr data to low doses, which in this experiment means average bone doses less than about 30 Gy, when the incidence of bone tumours fell to less than 10%. NCRP[3] derived an RBE_m for alpha particle irradiation of about 26 for the studies with beagle dogs and about 25 for mice at an incidence of bone sarcomas of about 8% and an average absorbed dose from ^{226}Ra of about 1 Gy. At low doses the increase in RBE resulted from a decrease in the risk per unit dose from ^{90}Sr rather than from an increase in the risk from ^{226}Ra.

13   Griffith *et al*[20] have compared the incidence of bone tumours in beagle dogs that inhaled either ^{90}SrCl$_2$ or ^{238}PuO$_2$. Several types of dose–response functions were used in calculating RBE values based on estimates of the dose to the endosteal cells on bone surfaces. A best estimate of RBE_m of 5.4 was obtained although other values in the range 4.0–5.8 were found.

Lung tumours in experimental animals

14   ICRP[21] reviewed a large amount of data on lung cancer in animals caused by alpha and beta emitters either inhaled or injected directly into the lungs. The doses quoted were averages to the whole lung from the time of inhalation or injection to the date of death. The animals used were predominantly rats but some data for mice and dogs were considered. There was considerable variation in the dose–response data but the

studies generally showed a greater effectiveness of alpha particle irradiation in inducing tumours. It was concluded that at low doses and low dose rates the RBE of inhaled alpha emitters compared with that of beta/gamma emitters was about 30. RBEs in the range 6-40 were obtained for dose-response relationships given in the report at 10% and 40% tumour incidence.

15   Further data for beagles from studies at the Inhalation Toxicology Research Institute in Albuquerque have indicated RBE values in the range 10–18 comparing lung tumour incidence resulting from exposure to the alpha emitter ^{239}PuO$_2$ with that obtained following exposure to the beta emitter ^{91}Y bound into insoluble fused aluminosilicate particles (FAP)[22].

16   A more recent analysis of data for both rats and beagles from the same laboratory has compared the effect of inhaling aerosols of ^{239}PuO$_2$ and the beta emitting fission products (^{90}Y, ^{91}Y, ^{144}Ce and ^{90}Sr in FAP) on lung tumour induction[23]. Alpha particle irradiation was more effective at inducing lung tumours than beta particle irradiation, on the basis of average lung dose. The RBE was found to be about 25 for rats and 36 for beagle dogs.

Studies on cells in culture

17   There are a number of mammalian cell lines available that can be transformed if irradiated in culture. The damage to the cell that causes this change is believed to be similar to the initial mutagenic change that occurs in somatic cells in body tissues which ultimately go on to develop cancer. Such studies may therefore be used to make an estimate of the RBE for tumour induction. *In vitro* systems have the advantage that they avoid the dosimetric complications of *in vivo* exposure. Other cellular studies have examined the effect of different radiations on the rate of mutation at specific gene loci in somatic cells in culture and for the induction of chromosome aberrations.

18   Brenner[24] analysed RBE$_m$ measurements for cell transformation in mouse fibroblast C3H10T$^{1/2}$ cells and described them in terms of energy deposition in small (subcellular) volumes. The value of RBE$_m$ was found to increase with the rate of energy transfer to tissue (measured in keV μm^{-1}), reaching a peak value at an LET of about 100 keV μm^{-1} and subsequently falling rapidly with increasing LET. For alpha particles with energies in the range 70–250 keV μm^{-1} values of RBE$_m$ ranging from 10 to 25 may be derived. The reduction in response above about 100 keV μm^{-1} can be accounted for by cell killing.

19   The effect of the rate of transfer of energy on mutation has been examined in experiments using human lung fibroblasts (HF19) and Chinese hamster (V79) cells and assaying induced thioguanine resistance (a mutagenic change)[25,26]. For both cell lines the highest value of RBE$_m$ occurred at LET values between 90 and 200 keV μm^{-1} which lie well within the range of LET for alpha emitters. For HF19 cells the maximum RBE$_m$ was 7.1 (at 90 keV μm^{-1}) compared with X-rays while for V79 cells it was 18 (at 110–200 keV μm^{-1}) compared with ^{60}Co gamma rays.

20   The observation of chromosome aberrations in human lymphocytes has produced qualitatively similar conclusions. A peaked dose–response relationship between RBE and LET has been derived from experiments with neutrons[27]. Data using alpha particles are consistent with this relationship. The peak value occurs at about 70 keV μm^{-1} and the RBE then drops rapidly with increase in LET. This sharp decrease occurs within the range of LET values exhibited by alpha particles and can be accounted for by cell

killing. Values of RBE_m ranging from 5 to 35 have been obtained depending on alpha particle energy[5,28].

21   Recent studies on the effects of alpha particle irradiation from [238]Pu on murine haemopoietic stem cells (from CBA/H mice) have shown a high frequency of non-clonal chromosome aberrations in the descendants of irradiated cells[29], a response not found in parallel studies with X-rays. This has been reported as implying very high (∞) RBE values. This alpha-particle-induced chromosomal instability appears to vary appreciably with the strain of mouse as a much reduced response has been found with haemopoietic stem cells from B6D2F1 mice[30]. It is not clear whether this effect of alpha particle irradiation on cells could be a contributor to the increased effectiveness of alpha irradiation in causing long-term effects in tissues, such as cancer. It may be that the chromosomal changes observed over a number of cell generations ultimately cause the premature death of cells as proposed by Mole[31], a point acknowledged by an author of the original paper[32]. However, no suggestion of very high RBE values for alpha-particle-induced tumour induction comes from either experimental data or epidemiological studies on humans exposed to alpha emitters (Chapter 4), reflecting the fact that both alpha particles and low LET radiation are implicated in tumour induction. Quantitative estimates of the risk of cancer from alpha particle irradiation are most appropriately based on epidemiological studies with the application of w_R values based on the most relevant RBEs.

Germ cell mutations

22   Some further evidence on RBE_m for alpha particles comes from Searle *et al*[33]. They investigated the effects of irradiation from [239]Pu on the germ cells of male mice following intravenous injection as the citrate complex. Three independent tests of effectiveness, the induction of chromosome fragments, chromosome translocations and dominant lethal lesions, all produced similar RBE_m values of 24, 24 and 22 for alpha particles compared with gamma rays.

Summary

23   This review of experimental data on the RBE_m for alpha particle irradiation relevant to tumour induction has demonstrated that a range of values has been obtained. Animal studies suggest a value of about 20 although there is some variation with a range of RBE values between about 5 and 40. For cellular studies RBE_m values lie largely in the range 10–35. These values are summarised in Table 7.3. On the basis of such data ICRP[12] has adopted a radiation weighting factor, w_R, for alpha particles of 20 for radiological protection purposes.

Epidemiological studies

24   A number of studies have been published on human populations exposed to alpha particle irradiation. These studies give only limited information from which RBE values for alpha emitters can be obtained as the patterns of exposure are not directly comparable. They do, however, provide direct information on tumour induction in humans exposed to internally incorporated alpha emitters. Data are available on the induction of bone, liver and lung tumours and of leukaemia. The studies available are summarised below.

Bone tumours

25   An increased incidence of cancer has been observed in people exposed to long-lived radium, particularly in painters of luminous dials, but also radium chemists or people

Endpoint	RBE	Reference
Bone tumours (dogs)	26	NCRP[3]
Bone tumours (mice)	25	NCRP[3]
Bone tumours (dogs)	5.4 (4.0–5.8)	Griffith et al[20]
Lung tumours (various species)	30 (6–40)	ICRP[21]
Lung tumours (dogs)	10–18	Boecker et al[22]
Lung tumours (rats)	25	Hahn et al[23]
Lung tumours (dogs)	36	Hahn et al[23]
Cell transformation (C3H10T½)	10–25	Brenner[24]
Cell mutation (human lung cells HF19)	Up to 7.1*	Cox and Masson[25]
Cell mutation (chinese hamster cells, V79)	Up to 18	Thacker et al[26]
Chromosome aberrations	5–35	Edwards et al[5] Purrott et al[28]
Germ cell mutations (chromosome fragments chromosome translocations, dominant lethals)	22–24	Searle et al[33]

TABLE 7.3
Summary of estimated RBE_m values for alpha particle irradiation, compared with gamma rays

*Compared with X-rays.

treated with alpha emitting radium salts for a supposedly therapeutic effect[34]. These people became internally contaminated with pure ^{226}Ra ($t½$ = 1600 years) in some cases, and in other cases with various mixtures of ^{226}Ra and ^{228}Ra ($t½$ = 5.8 years). These long-lived radium isotopes deposit mainly in the skeleton where they irradiate the cells on bone surfaces and the bone marrow. By the end of 1983, 62 cases of bone sarcoma and 32 cases of head sinus carcinoma had occurred in a total of 2352 people who had been measured to obtain an estimate of their body content of radium and hence to be able to calculate radiation dose. The majority of the bone sarcomas and head cancers had appeared by 1969, although three bone tumours have appeared since then and head cancers have recently appeared at a greater rate than bone cancers.

The effect of intakes of radium has also been studied in German patients injected with alpha emitting ^{224}Ra ($t½$ = 3.6 days) shortly after World War II. The study group consists of a population of 681 adults and 218 juveniles (age at first injection varied between 1 and 20 years) who received weekly or twice weekly intravenous injections of ^{224}Ra, mainly for the treatment of bone tuberculosis or ankylosing spondylitis[35]. The follow-up times from first injection to death or last known health status ranged from 0 to 38 years and averaged 22 years. By June 1984 half of the patients were known to have died. As with the ^{226}Ra cases bone sarcoma has been the main effect of intakes of ^{224}Ra, with 54 cases observed (36 in juveniles and 18 in adults) compared with only 0.2 expected naturally. The last bone tumour occurred in 1983, 33 years after the injection of ^{224}Ra into a 3 year old boy and is the only bone sarcoma reported in this series since 1974. Very few new tumours are now expected. These data suggest that radiation-induced bone sarcomas have a period of expression similar to that for leukaemia.

27   Based on these studies, particularly that of the ^{224}Ra patients, ICRP[12] adopted a risk estimate for bone tumour mortality of $5\ 10^{-4}$ Sv^{-1} (assuming a w_R of 20 for alpha particle irradiation). As emphasised by Puskin *et al*[36], this estimate refers to the average skeletal dose.

28   The data from the follow-up of the atomic bomb survivors at Hiroshima and Nagasaki can be used to provide an estimate of the risk of bone tumours resulting from exposure to (predominantly) low LET gamma radiation. The excess relative risk for bone cancer mortality in this population can be obtained from the data file employed by Shimizu *et al*[37] in analyses of the non-cancer data[38]. The excess relative risk coefficient is $7.7\ 10^{-1}$ Sv^{-1} (95% CI < 0, 4.29) which would correspond to a risk of fatal bone cancer in the population of England and Wales of about $2.2\ 10^{-4}$ Sv^{-1} (95% CI < 0, 12.4)[38]. This is a risk based on exposures at high dose rates and needs to be modified to assess risks at low doses and low dose rates. The reduction factor included to allow for repair of damage at low doses and low dose rates (usually termed a dose and dose rate effectiveness factor, DDREF) most recently recommended by ICRP[12] is 2. The risk of bone cancer at low doses and low dose rates thus becomes $1.1\ 10^{-4}$ Sv^{-1}.

29   These two estimates of the risk of bone tumours ($5\ 10^{-4}$ Sv^{-1} and $1.1\ 10^{-4}$ Sv^{-1}) are based on quite different populations and patterns of exposure. Given the wide confidence limits on the data from the atomic bomb survivors, they are not inconsistent with each other.

Lung tumours

30   As described in Chapter 4, increased mortality from lung cancer has been observed in a range of studies of underground miners exposed to ^{222}Rn and its alpha emitting decay products. Based on some of these studies the BEIR IV Committee has estimated[39] the risk of lung cancer following exposure to radon and its decay products to be 350 deaths per 10^6 people exposed per WLM. This corresponds to an individual risk of $4.2\ 10^{-3}$ Sv^{-1} following exposure of the lung ($3.5\ 10^{-2}$ Sv^{-1}, effective dose), assuming a radiation weighting factor, w_R, for alpha irradiation of 20.

31   In its most recent recommendations ICRP[12] has estimated the risk of lung cancer in a working population to be $6.8\ 10^{-3}$ Sv^{-1} (using a DDREF of 2). This risk estimate was based on the follow-up study of the atomic bomb survivors, and applies to a world population. The risk of lung cancer in a UK working population derived in this report is $1.4\ 10^{-2}$ Sv^{-1} (Table 4.5), again based on a DDREF for low LET radiation of 2.

32   The relative similarity in risk factors developed from the miners exposed predominantly to alpha particle irradiation and from a Japanese population exposed

predominantly to gamma rays, suggests that the choice of a w_R of 20 for alpha irradiation is reasonably consistent with the data.

Liver tumours

33   Thorotrast is colloidal thorium oxide and emits alpha particles. In the late 1920s it began to be injected into the arteries of patients for use in diagnostic radiology as it was an effective X-ray contrast material. Extensive epidemiological studies in a number of countries, including Denmark, Germany, Japan, Portugal, Sweden and the USA, have shown that retention of thorium oxide particles in the liver and in the bone marrow has resulted in an increased risk of liver tumours and leukaemias as well as liver cirrhosis and other cardiovascular diseases[40]. On the basis of an injected dose of 25 ml the dose rate to the liver is estimated to be 0.25 Gy y^{-1}. Present estimates, based on a latent period of 20 years, suggest a lifetime risk of liver cancer following exposure to Thorotrast of about $1.5 \ 10^{-3}$ Sv^{-1} (assuming a w_R of 20 for alpha particle irradiation)[12,39]; about half this risk is expected to be expressed by 40 years after exposure.

34   The excess relative risk coefficient for liver cancer incidence in the atomic bomb survivors given by Thompson *et al*[41] is 0.49 Sv^{-1} (90% CI = 0.16, 0.92). With these figures, the risk of fatal liver cancer for the population of England and Wales is calculated[38] to be $1.07 \ 10^{-3}$ Sv^{-1}. Application of a DDREF of 2 gives a risk at low doses of $5.3 \ 10^{-4}$ Sv^{-1}. Again the similarity of the results obtained for alpha particle irradiation and for low LET radiation suggests the choice of an RBE of 20 for alpha particle irradiation is not unreasonable.

Leukaemia

35   Radiation-induced leukaemias also occurred as a late effect in the Thorotrast patients, presumably as a result of irradiation of stem cells in the bone marrow. A recent estimate[40] of the risk is about $5.5 \ 10^{-3}$ Gy^{-1}, with a possible lifetime risk of $6 \ 10^{-3}$ to $7 \ 10^{-3}$ Gy^{-1}. This is very close to the ICRP estimate[12] of the risk of leukaemia based on the follow-up of the atomic bomb survivors ($5 \ 10^{-3}$ Sv^{-1}) implying that in this instance the RBE may be near unity. This result may possibly be influenced by the effect of cell killing in the bone marrow.

Summary

36   The available epidemiological studies do not provide ideal sets of data on which to base estimates of the RBE for tumour induction from alpha particle irradiation because of the need to make comparisons between, rather than within, studies. Features such as the patterns of exposure are different in the groups being compared. However, for tumours of the liver, lung and bone, and for leukaemia, data are available which suggest that the adoption of a quality factor of 20 is not unreasonable (Table 7.4).

Conclusions

37   The information relevant to the choice of an appropriate value of the RBE for alpha particle irradiation has been reviewed. The short track length of alpha particles, together with uncertainties on the relative positions in tissues of alpha emitting radionuclides and the target cells, creates difficulties in specifying dose and therefore in making judgements on an appropriate value for the quality factor (or w_R). Experimental data in animals give an RBE for alpha-particle-induced lung tumour and bone sarcoma induction between about 5 and 40, while cellular endpoints suggest similar values (10–35). The data available from human populations exposed both to low LET radiation

and to alpha emitters suggest that a rounded RBE of 20 based on experimental studies is reasonable, although the human information is rather limited.

AUGER ELECTRON EMITTERS

38   Although rarely encountered compared with exposures to neutron and alpha particle radiations, Auger emitters provide a particularly difficult problem for risk assessment. ICRP[12] gives only generalised advice stating that microdosimetric techniques need to be applied. The problem arises because electrons emitted in Auger cascades have a range of only a few hundred nanometres at most and therefore deposit energy very close to the site of decay. If the Auger emitters are located preferentially within the cell nucleus, then greater damage ensues. Some experimental evidence for this increased damage is presented occasionally and the proceedings of a recent workshop have been published[42]. Kassis *et al*[43] using V79 cells irradiation *in vitro* with several radionuclides and Rao *et al*[44] using sperm head observations following testicular irradiation of mice with ^{201}Tl show this increased effect for cell killing. Unfortunately, very little data exist for cell mutation and transformation endpoints and no data exist for cancer in animals. The limited published data support the effects seen for cell killing.

39   Calculations have shown that expressing results in terms of mean dose to the cell nucleus is in some instances successful in explaining the increased effect[45]. However, if the Auger emitter is incorporated as part of the chromatin a greater biological effect ensues than would be expected on the basis of average nuclear dose. Charlton[46] has by Monte Carlo simulation calculated the number of double strand breaks produced by chromatin incorporated ^{125}I and finds about a factor of five increase compared with the same nuclear dose of X-rays. This is close to the experimental value for killing of V79 cells *in vitro*[43].

TABLE 7.4
Epidemiological studies considered for RBE values

Tumour	Study	Risk coefficient
Bone	[226]Ra workers[a] ⎫ [224]Ra medical[a] ⎬	$5 \ 10^{-4} \ Sv^{-1}$
	Atomic bomb survivors[b]	$1.1 \ 10^{-4} \ Sv^{-1}$
Lung	Miners[a]	$4.2 \ 10^{-3} \ Sv^{-1}$
	Atomic bomb survivors[b]	$6.8 \ 10^{-3} \ Sv^{-1}$
Liver	Thorotrast injection[a]	$1.5 \ 10^{-3} \ Sv^{-1}$
	Atomic bomb survivors[b]	$5.3 \ 10^{-4} \ Sv^{-1}$
Leukaemia	Thorotrast injection[a,c]	$6 \ 10^{-3}$ to $7 \ 10^{-3} \ Gy^{-1}$
	Atomic bomb survivors[b]	$5 \ 10^{-3} \ Sv^{-1}$

Notes
(a) Alpha particle irradiation, assumes weighting factor, $w_R = 20$.
(b) Low LET radiation, assumes a dose and dose rate effectiveness factor (DDREF) of 2 (ICRP[12]).
(c) No weighting factor, w_R, for alpha irradiation applied.

40   In summary, there is some evidence for the increased effect of Auger emitters even when dosimetry is based on the estimation of doses to the cell nucleus. Much detailed information is required to assess the risk. The concentration of the Auger emitter within the cell nucleus is dependent on its chemical form. If the Auger emitter is not attached to the chromatin then estimation of dose to the nucleus seems an adequate representation of the biological effect. If the Auger emitter is attached to the chromatin then the biological effect is characteristic of a high LET response and a further factor is required. This factor depends on the physical decay scheme and is therefore nuclide dependent. For the present there are insufficient data available to make any general recommendations for calculating doses. In the case of a few specific Auger emitters some allowance may need to be made for this heterogeneity of distribution in calculating doses for assessing risk.

CONCLUSIONS

41   The information relevant to a judgement of radiation weighting factors (w_R) has been summarised. The relative biological effectiveness for fission neutrons with respect to gamma rays for cancer endpoints in animals is in the range 5–20 (on the assumption of a DDREF of 2 for low LET radiation). RBE_m values for cellular endpoints suggest values towards the higher end of this range. The variation of w_R with neutron energy is in reasonable agreement with cellular data on RBE_m and thus w_R values recommended by ICRP are considered appropriate.

42   The short track length of alpha particles, together with uncertainties on the relative positions in tissues of alpha emitting radionuclides and target cells, creates great difficulties in specifying dose and therefore in making judgements on an appropriate value for w_R. On the basis of average organ dose the RBE for bone and lung tumour induction by alpha particles in experimental animals may vary between about 5 and 40, while cellular endpoints suggest similar values (10–35). Despite these uncertainties the alpha particle w_R of 20 recommended by ICRP[12] does not appear to be unreasonable.

43   For radionuclides emitting Auger electrons, although rarely encountered, the assessment of risk requires the calculation of nuclear dose. In addition, if the radionuclide is predominantly attached to the chromatin then this may also need to be considered. There are, however, insufficient data available to make any general recommendations.

REFERENCES

1   Sinclair, W K. Experimental RBE value of high LET radiations at low doses and the implications for quality factor assignment. *Radiat. Prot. Dosim.* **13**, 319–26 (1985).

2   UNSCEAR. Ionising radiation: sources and biological effects. Report to the General Assembly, with annexes. New York, United Nations (1982).

3   NCRP. The relative biological effectiveness of radiations of different quality. Bethesda, MD, National Council on Radiation Protection and Measurements. Report No. 104 (1990).

4   ICRP. RBE for deterministic effects. ICRP Publication 58. *Ann. ICRP.* **20**, No. 4 (1989).

5   Edwards, A A, Purrott, R J, Prosser J S, *et al.* The induction of chromosome aberrations in human lymphocytes by alpha-radiation. *Int. J. Radiat. Biol.* **38**, 83–91 (1980).

6   Bilbao, A J S, Prosser, A A, Edwards, *et al.* The induction of micronuclei in human lymphocytes by *in vitro* irradiation with alpha particles from plutonium-239. *Int. J. Radiat. Biol.*, **56**, 287–92 (1989).

7   Blocher, D. DNA double-strand break repair determines the RBE of α-particles. *Int. J. Radiat. Biol.,* **54,** 761–71 (1988).

8   Aghamohammadi, S Z, Goodhead, D T, and Savage, J R K. Induction of sister chromatid exchanges (SCE) in G lymphocytes by plutonium-238 α-particles. *Int. J. Radiat. Biol.,* **53,** 909–15 (1988).

9   Nagasawa, H, and Little, J B. Induction of sister chromatid exchanges by extremely low doses of α-particles. *Cancer Res.,* **52,** 6394–6 (1992).

10   Rao, D V, Narra, V R, Howell, R G, *et al.* Induction of sperm head abnormalities by incorporated radionuclides: Dependence on subcellular distribution, type of radiation, dose rate and presence of radioprotectors. *Radiat. Res.,* **125,** 89–97 (1991).

11   UNSCEAR. Genetic and somatic effects of ionising radiation. Report to the General Assembly, with annexes. New York, United Nations (1986).

12   ICRP. 1990 Recommendations of the International Commission on Radiological Protection. ICRP Publication 60. *Ann. ICRP,* **21,** Nos 1–3 (1991).

13   Hei, T K, Hall, E J, and Waldren, C A. Neutron risk assessment based on low dose mutation data. IN *Low Dose Radiation. Biological Bases for Risk Assessment* (Eds K F Baverstock and J W Stather). London, Taylor and Francis, pp 481–90 (1989).

14   Miller, R C, Geard, C R, Brenner, D J, Komatsu, K, Marino, S A, and Hall, E J. Neutron energy-dependent oncogenic transformation of C3H 10T½ mouse cell. *Radiat. Res.,* **117,** 114–27 (1989).

15   Sevan'kaev, A V, Zherbin, E A, Luchnik, N V, *et al.* Cytogenic effects produced by neutrons in lymphocytes of human peripheral blood *in vitro.* 1. Dose–response dependence of neutrons of different energies for different types of chromosomal aberrations. *Genetika-USSR,* **15,** 1046–60 (1979) (In Russian).

16   NCRP. Protection against neutron radiation. Bethesda, MD, National Council on Radiation Protection and Measurements, Report No. 38 (1971).

17   Miller, S C and Buster, D S. Tabular data on the experimental dogs IN Research in Radiobiology. Salt Lake City, University of Utah, Report COO-119-262, p A1 (1986).

18   Finkel, M P, Biskis, B O, and Scribner, G M. The influence of strontium-90 upon lifespan and neoplasms of mice. IN *Progress in Nuclear Energy,* Series IV, Volume 2 – Biological Sciences, New York, Pergamon Press, p 199 (1959).

19   Finkel, M P, Biskis, B O, and Jinkins, P B. Toxicity of radium-226 in mice. IN *Radiation Induced Cancer,* (Ed A Ericson). Vienna, IAEA, p 369 (1969).

20   Griffith, W C, Boecker, B B, Gillett, N A, *et al.* Comparison of risk factors for bone cancer induced by inhaled ^{90}SrCl$_2$ and ^{238}PuO$_2$. IN *Proceedings EULEP/DoE Joint Bone Radiobiology Workshop,* Toronto, July, 1991. Washington DC, USDOE Report UCD-472-136 (1991).

21   ICRP. Biological effects of inhaled radionuclides. ICRP Publication 31. *Ann. ICRP,* **4,** Nos 1–2 (1980).

22   Boecker, B B, Hahn F F, Muggenburg, B A, Guilmette, R A, Griffith, W C, and McClellan, R O. The relative effectiveness of inhaled alpha and beta-emitting radionuclides in producing lung cancer. IN *Proceedings IRPA7: 7th International Congress of the International Radiation Protection Association,* April 1988, Sydney, Pergamon Press, Volume 2, 1059–62 (1988).

23   Hahn, F F, *et al.* Comparison of the effects of inhaled ^{239}PuO$_2$ and β-emitting radionuclides on the incidence of lung carcinomas in laboratory animals. IN *Proceedings IRPA8: 8th International Congress of the International Radiation Protection Association,* Montreal, May 1991. London, Pergamon Press, Volume 1, pp 916–19 (1991).

24   Brenner, D J. The microdosimetry of radon daughters and its significance. *Radiat. Prot. Dosim.,* **31,** 399–403 (1990).

25   Cox, R, and Masson, W K. Mutation and activation of cultured mammalian cells exposed to beams of accelerated heavy ions. III. Human diploid fibroblasts. *Int. J. Radiat. Biol,* **36,** 149–60 (1979).

26   Thacker, J, Stretch, A and Stephens, M A. Mutation and inactivation of cultured mammalian cells exposed to beams of accelerated heavy ions. II. Chinese hamster V79 cells. *Int. J. Radiat. Biol.,* **36,** 137–48 (1979).

27   Edwards, A A, Lloyd, D C, and Prosser, J S. Chromosome aberrations in human lymphocytes. A radiobiological review. IN *Low Dose Radiation, Biological Bases for Risk Assessment* (Eds K F Baverstock and J W Stather). London, Taylor and Francis, pp 423–32 (1989).

28   Purrott, R J, Edwards, A A, Lloyd, D C, and Stather, J W. The induction of chromosome aberrations in human lymphocytes by *in vitro* irradiation with α-particles from plutonium-239. *Int. J. Radiat. Biol.,* **38,** 277–84 (1980).

29   Kadhim, M A, Macdonald, D A, Goodhead, D T, *et al.* Transmission of chromosomal instability after plutonium α-particle irradiation. *Nature*, **355**, 738–40 (1992).

30   Kadhim, M A, Lorimore, S A, Buckle, V J, *et al.* Alpha-particle irradiation of human bone marrow cells (Abs). Manchester, UKCCCR 3rd Grant Holders Meeting, January (1993).

31   Mole, R H. Alpha-particles and leukaemia (Letter). *Nature*, **357**, 369–70 (1992).

32   Wright, E. Reply to Mole, R H (Letter). *Nature*, **357**, 370 (1992).

33   Searle, A G, Beechey, C V, Green, D, and Humphreys, E R. Cytogenetic effects of protracted exposures to alpha particles from ^{239}Pu and to gamma rays from ^{60}Co compared in male mice. *Mutat. Res.*, **41**, 297–310 (1976).

34   Rundo, J, Keane, A T, Lucas, H F, *et al.* Current (1984) status of the study of ^{226}Ra and ^{228}Ra in humans at the Center for Human Biology. IN Proceedings Symposium: *The Radiobiology of Radium and Thorotrast* (Eds W Gössner, G B Gerber, U Hagen and A Luz). *Strahlentherapie*, **80**, Suppl. 14–21 (1986).

35   Mays, C W, Spiess, H, Chemelevsky, D, and Kellerer, A. Bone sarcoma cumulative tumor rates in patients injected with ^{224}Ra. IN Proceedings Symposium: *The Radiobiology of Radium and Thorotrast* (Eds W Gössner, G B Gerber, U Hagen and A Luz). *Strahlentherapie*, **80**, Suppl. 27–31 (1986).

36   Puskin, J S, Nelson, N S, and Nelson, C B. Bone cancer risk estimates. *Health Phys.*, **63**, 579–80 (1992).

37   Shimizu, Y, Kato, H, Schull, W J, and Hoel, D G. Studies of the mortality of A-bomb survivors. 9. Mortality, 1950–1985: Part 3. Noncancer mortality based on the revised doses (DS 86). *Radiat. Res.*, **130**, 249–66 (1992).

38   Little, M. NRPB, Private communication (1993).

39   BEIR IV. Health risks of radon and other internally deposited alpha-emitters. Washington DC, NAS/NRC (1988).

40   van Kaick, G, Muth, H, and Kaul, A. The German Thorotrast Study. Report No. 1. Luxembourg, CEC, EUR 9504 EN (quoted in BEIR IV) (1984).

41   Thompson, D, Mabuchi, K, Ron, E, *et al.* Solid tumor incidence in A-bomb survivors, 1958–87. Hiroshima, Radiation Effects Research Foundation, Report TR5-92 (1993).

42   Baverstock, K F, and Charlton, D E (eds). *DNA Damage by Auger Emitters*. London, Taylor and Francis (1988).

43   Kassis, A I, Howell, R W, Sastry, K S R, and Adelstein, S J. Positional effects of Auger decays in mammalian cells in culture. IN *DNA Damage by Auger Emitters* (Eds K F Baverstock and D E Charlton). London, Taylor and Francis, pp 1–14 (1988).

44   Rao, D V, Mylavarapu, V B, Sastry, K S R, and Howell, R S. Internal Auger-emitters: Effects on spermatogenesis and oogenesis in mice. IN *DNA Damage by Auger Emitters*, (Eds K F Baverstock and D E Charlton). London, Taylor and Francis, pp 15–26 (1988).

45   Sastry, K S R, Howell, R W, Rao, D V, Mylavarapu, V B, Kassis, A I, Adelstein, S J, Wright, H A, Hamm, R N, and Turner, J E. Dosimetry of Auger emitters: Physical and phenomenological approaches. IN *DNA Damage by Auger Emitters* (Eds K F Baverstock and D E Charlton). London, Taylor and Francis, pp 27–38 (1988).

46   Charlton, D E. Calculation of single and double strand DNA breakage from incorporated ^{125}I. IN *DNA Damage by Auger Emitters* (Eds K F Baverstock and D E Charlton). London, Taylor and Francis, pp 89–100 (1988).

47   Edwards, A A, Lloyd, D C, and Prosser, J S. The induction of chromosome aberrations in human lymphocytes by accelerated charged particles. *Radiat. Prot. Dosim.*, **13**, 205–9 (1985).

48   Edwards, A A, Lloyd, D C, and Prosser, J S. The induction of chromosome aberrations in human lymphocytes by 24 keV neutrons. *Radiat. Prot. Dosim.*, **31**, 265–8 (1990).

8 Designation of Low Doses and Low Dose Rates for Low LET Radiation

PHYSICAL AND BIOLOGICAL FACTORS

1   The choice of bands for low and high doses and dose rates that are appropriate for decisions on whether to apply dose and dose rate effectiveness factors for low LET radiation is not straightforward, as it is essential to understand both the physical and biological factors involved and their possible interactions. In the UNSCEAR 1986 Report[1], low doses were taken to be those up to 0.2 Gy of low LET radiation, while those in the interval 2.0–3.5 Gy were regarded as high doses, with intermediate doses lying between these ranges. Low and high dose rates were taken to be below 70 mGy per day and above 70 Gy per day, respectively. The choice of 70 mGy per day appears to have come directly from animal studies which have indicated that dose rates below about 100 mGy per day of low LET radiation can be taken to be low dose rate and for which a DDREF can be applied (Chapter 3, Table 3.3). It should be noted that this 'low' dose rate is substantially higher than might be expected in cases of human exposure. ICRP[2] has recently recommended for radiation workers an average annual dose limit of 20 mSv: for members of the public 1 mSv y^{-1} is recommended, in addition to the dose from natural background radiation. In practice, most workers receive doses much lower than the dose limit. In the case of accidents, however, people may be exposed to high doses and high dose rates in which case the application of a DDREF would not be appropriate. There will also be individuals exposed over short periods of the working day to substantially higher dose rates than the average, although total doses are low (eg radiographers in hospitals). Thus information is needed on the magnitude of the dose and dose rate from low LET radiation below which a DDREF may apply. Several approaches may be used for determining such a boundary.

2   The microdosimetry approach for assessing low doses makes use of statistical considerations of energy deposition in cells. Gamma rays deposit electrons in cell nuclei and the smallest insult a cell can receive is one electron crossing its nucleus. This deposits, on average, about 1 or 2 mGy in a nucleus of 8 μm diameter[3]. If the induction of cancer at low doses depends on energy deposition in single cells, with no interaction between cells, there can be no departure from linearity unless there are at least two independent electron tracks in each cell nucleus. The number of tracks within the cells follows a Poisson distribution. Therefore for average tissue doses of 0.2 mGy or less, where most of the cell nuclei have no energy deposited in them, halving the dose merely halves the number of cells receiving energy depositions. For biological endpoints which are caused by energy deposited in one cell the dose–effect curve must be linear at these low doses. The effects must also be independent of dose rate because this only affects the time interval between energy deposited in different cells. This argument depends initially on the size of the sensitive volume which may be less than that of the nucleus. If this were the case, then the estimate of a low dose, at which there would be no opportunity for interaction between events, would increase.

3   A second argument can be used to derive a value for a low dose. From animal experiments, about 0.06 mGy min^{-1} given over a few days or weeks has been demonstrated to be a low dose rate (Table 3.3). From this an estimate can be made of a low dose if it is assumed that dose rate effects arise from a sufficient accumulation of damage in a cell within repair times characteristic of DNA damage, say a few hours. On this basis about 20 mGy may be regarded as a low dose. It is noteworthy, however, that experimental studies at 'high' dose rates were frequently undertaken in the range 100–800 mGy min^{-1} (150–1200 Gy d^{-1}) (Table 3.3), ie dose rates more than one-thousand times those at the 'low' dose rates for which a DDREF in the range of about 2–10 has been obtained. It is possible that a similar tumour yield to that obtained at 100 mGy d^{-1} could have been obtained at dose rates a few times higher than this. There are possibly analogies here with data on mutation yield in mouse spermatogonia for which a three-fold reduction in yield was obtained at 8 mGy min^{-1} compared with 720–900 mGy min^{-1} (Chapter 3, paragraph 38), with no further reduction at 0.007 mGy min^{-1} (10 mGy d^{-1}).

4   A third approach to estimating low doses comes from direct observations of cellular effects. As described earlier, in Chapter 3, the incidence, I, of an effect can frequently be related to dose, D, by an equation of the form:

$$I(D) = \alpha_1 D + \alpha_2 D^2$$

in which α_1 and α_2, the coefficients for the linear and quadratic terms for the radiation response, are fitted constants and are different for different endpoints. This equation has been shown to fit data on the induction of chromosome aberrations in human lymphocytes, for example, and also data on cell killing and mutation induction. For chromosome aberrations in human lymphocytes, the value of α_1/α_2 is about 200 mGy for ^{60}Co gamma rays, and thus the response is essentially linear up to 20 mGy, the square-term contributing only 10% of the total[4]. On this basis it could therefore be estimated that < 20 mGy is a low dose.

5   A fourth approach to estimating a low dose is based on the analysis of data from epidemiological studies, in particular from data on the survivors of the atomic bombings in Japan. Analysis of the dose response for mortality from solid cancers[5] in the range 0–4 Gy (adjusted for random error) has suggested α_1/α_2 ratios from a minimum of about 1 Gy with a best estimate of about 5 Gy. This would suggest a low dose of at least 100 mGy, which may be the most appropriate figure for the endpoint of concern here. There is, in practice, little evidence of a departure from linearity up to about 3 Gy.

CONCLUSIONS

6   A number of approaches have been examined for determining low doses and low dose rates at which a DDREF may be applied. Experimental studies suggest that dose rates of about 0.1 mGy min^{-1} are low, whatever the total dose. Radiobiological experiments suggest that acute doses of about 20 mGy are low, although epidemiological studies suggest a low dose is at least 100 mGy, whatever the dose rate. It may be concluded that, for the purposes of applying dose rate effectiveness factors in radiation protection, dose rates of less than about 0.1 mGy min^{-1} (when averaged over about 1 hour) and acute doses of less than about 100 mGy may be regarded as low.

REFERENCES

1   UNSCEAR. Genetic and somatic effects of ionizing radiation. 1986 Report to the General Assembly, with annexes. New York, United Nations (1986).

2   ICRP. 1990 Recommendations of the International Commission on Radiological Protection. ICRP Publication 60. *Ann. ICRP*, **21**, Nos 1–3 (1991).

3   Booz, J, and Feinendegen, L E. A microdosimetric understanding of low-dose radiation effects. *Int. J. Radiat. Biol.*, **53**, 1–12 (1988).

4   Lloyd, D C, and Edwards, A A. Chromosome aberrations in human lymphocytes: Effect of radiation quality, dose and dose rate. IN *Radiation-induced Chromosome Damage in Man* (Eds T Ishima and M S Sasaki). New York, A R Liss, pp 23–49 (1983).

5   Pierce, D A, and Vaeth, M. The shape of the cancer mortality dose–response curve for atomic bomb survivors. Hiroshima, Radiation Effects Research Foundation, Report TR7-89 (1989).

9 Executive Summary

1   In this document the data that provide a basis for the assessment of the human health consequences following exposure of a UK population to external radiation and intakes of radioactive materials have been reviewed. The main focus of the document is on the stochastic effects of radiation, ie the induction of cancer and heritable effects, and for these, outlines of the current understanding of the mechanisms of induction as well as estimates of risk coefficients are provided. Acute deterministic effects of radiation are not, in general, included in this document but effects of *in utero* irradiation, particularly those relating to the early development of the brain, are reviewed. Much of the information contained here is developed from that reviewed and used by UNSCEAR[1], BEIR[2] and ICRP[3] and by the Board[4]. Other published sources are also extensively drawn upon.

2   The aim of this document is to consider the scientific evidence from which assessments of late health effects can be based and to consider the associated uncertainties. The UK-specific risk factors developed in this document for cancer induction are not intended to replace those that ICRP[3] has developed for setting standards in radiation protection. They are, however, for use in calculating late health effects within a UK population, eg in accident consequence assessments or in determining probability of causation. Particular attention has also been given to reviewing the risks to the developing embryo and fetus.

3   The development of cancer is the major late effect resulting from exposure to radiation. There is much new information on the cellular and molecular mechanisms that drive the complex multistage tumorigenic process. From these data it is argued that the induction of gene mutations in single target somatic cells in tissue underlies the induction of cancer by radiation: the importance of cellular DNA repair processes for low dose and low dose rate response and radiation quality effects are also outlined together with evidence that, in a small fraction of the population, cancer susceptibility may be principally determined by inherited factors. Whereas definitive statements are not yet possible, current understanding of carcinogenic mechanisms and DNA repair would suggest that a low dose threshold for cancer induction by radiation should not be expected. Attention is also drawn to advances in the molecular genetics of cancer that highlight the possibility that radiation-induced tumours may carry gene mutations characteristic of radiation damage.

4   The risks of radiation-induced cancer derived from studies of the Japanese atomic bomb survivors and medically exposed groups are based largely on exposures to high doses received at high dose rates. In contrast to this, for radiological protection purposes, the principal concern is that of radiation effects at low doses and low dose rates. Experimental studies using whole animal, cellular and molecular systems have clearly shown that for low LET radiation the expression of radiation-induced damage increases with dose and is also usually greater when a given dose is received at high rather than low dose rates. Studies with cellular systems suggest that the efficiency and fidelity of DNA repair is a major determining factor for these effects.

5   The reduced effect of low dose and low dose rate exposure is estimated with a dose and dose rate effectiveness factor (DDREF). Information on cancer incidence in the Japanese atomic bomb survivors may be used to derive a DDREF of around 1.5 in order to estimate human cancer risk at low dose and low dose rates. A review of relevant animal tumorigenesis provides, however, values of DDREF in the range 1 to > 10. These data show that although dose–effect relationships for cancer induction may frequently be fitted by a linear–quadratic function it is not always possible to resolve the common linear term that defines the low dose and low dose rate response. Thus, it may be that at lower dose rates than those experienced by the Japanese atomic bomb survivors, a DDREF > 1.5 may apply. Risk estimates derived from limited data on the effects of human exposure at low dose rates do not, however, support the use of high DDREF values, and it is not considered appropriate to apply the relatively high DDREF values obtained in some animal studies for human risk assessment. In consideration of these data and in recognition of the uncertainties involved, a DDREF of 2 is adopted here for the estimation of cancer risk coefficients applying to all tissues. A DDREF value of 2 has also been recommended by ICRP[3]. For high LET radiation no DDREF should be applied.

6   Consideration has been given to the choice of bands for low and high doses and dose rates for application in radiological protection. It is concluded that for the purposes of applying dose and dose rate effectiveness factors, dose rates of less than about 0.1 mGy min^{-1} (when averaged over about 1 hour) and acute doses of less than about 100 mGy may be regarded as low.

7   The information relevant to the judgement of radiation weighting factors, w_R, has been summarised. The relative biological effectiveness for fission neutrons with respect to gamma rays for cancer endpoints in animals is in the range 5–20 (assuming a DDREF of 2 for low LET radiation). RBE_m values for cellular endpoints suggest values towards the higher end of this range. The variation of w_R with neutron energy is found to be in reasonable agreement with cellular data on RBE_m: thus w_R values recommended by ICRP[3] are considered appropriate.

8   The short track length of alpha particles, together with uncertainties on the relative positions in tissues of alpha emitting radionuclides and target cells, creates great difficulties in specifying dose and therefore in making judgements on an appropriate value for w_R. From average organ dose, it is found that alpha particle RBE values for animal bone and lung tumours may vary between about 5 and 40, whereas cellular endpoints suggest similar values in the range 10–35. Despite these uncertainties the alpha particle w_R of 20 recommended by ICRP[3] does not appear to be unreasonable.

9   Information on radiation-induced cancer risks has been obtained from a variety of epidemiological studies of human populations. Of these studies, that of the Japanese atomic bomb survivors is of substantial value in deriving risk estimates, owing to the large population size, the length of follow-up, the inclusion of people of all ages and both sexes, the availability on an individual basis of dose estimates for a wide range of organs, and the wide range of doses received. Information from studies of medically and occupationally exposed groups is utilised as supporting and additional evidence for specific cancer types. The models used in previous risk assessments to describe variations in risk with time since exposure and across populations have had an empirical basis. Other models are available that aim to provide a description of the carcinogenic

process. Although there is evidence for the multistage nature of tumorigenesis, current knowledge is insufficient to allow these mechanistic models to form the basis of risk estimation. Thus, although some illustrative calculations have been performed based on a particular type of mechanistic model, empirical models provide the basis of the risk estimates given below.

10   In the projection of risks of solid cancers over time, there are still uncertainties whether relative risks decrease at long times after exposure. There are also suggestions of different temporal patterns for different cancer types. In particular, the study of UK ankylosing spondylitis patients given X-ray therapy and, to some extent, the Japanese data suggest a decrease in the relative risk of lung cancer over time, whereas there is less evidence of a decrease in the relative risk of digestive cancers. To emphasise the uncertainties, risks based on a relative risk projection over a lifetime and up to 40 years following exposure have been calculated for most solid tumours: for lung cancer, the BEIR V time varying relative risk model was used[2]. Further follow-up of irradiated groups will be important in reducing this source of uncertainty.

11   In order to transfer radiation-induced cancer risks across populations with differing baseline rates, the available data, such as those for stomach and skin cancer, generally favour use of a multiplicative model transfer. However, there are still uncertainties in the transfer of risks from the Japanese data to a western population, particularly for breast cancer. Consequently, even though a multiplicative transfer from the Japanese survivor data has generally been used, data from western populations have been utilised for breast, thyroid, skin, bone and liver cancer. Further parallel analyses of irradiated groups with differing baseline cancer rates may help reduce the uncertainty in transferring risks across populations.

12   Analyses of the manner in which cancer risks of human populations vary with dose show that the data in these studies are generally consistent with a linear dose–response model, but are also consistent with linear–quadratic models under which the slope of the dose–response decreases with decreasing dose. For leukaemia, a model of the latter type provides a statistically significant improvement in fit to the Japanese survivor data in comparison with a linear model. Although epidemiological studies of low dose rate exposure should be more relevant for the purposes of radiological protection than studies at high dose rates, the former type of study at present lacks the statistical power to allow risks to be estimated with tight confidence limits. However, the results of studies such as those of radiation workers are consistent with risk estimates derived from high dose rate studies to which a DDREF of 2 (as described above) has been applied.

13   Based on the foregoing considerations, the total risk of radiation-induced cancer mortality in a UK population of all ages and both sexes exposed to low LET radiation at low doses and low dose rates is estimated at about 6.0×10^{-2} Sv^{-1}. This value is somewhat higher than the ICRP estimate[3] for a world population of 5.0×10^{-2} Sv^{-1}, owing to some differences in the models used and to slightly higher baseline cancer rates in the UK compared with a world average. It is also higher than the value of 4.5×10^{-2} Sv^{-1} given in NRPB–R226[4], owing primarily to a change in DDREF from 3 for most organs to 2 for all organs. However, there is still uncertainty associated with the projection of risks over time: the risk estimated here for a UK population for the period up to 40 years following exposure is 2.4×10^{-2} Sv^{-1}, ie about 40% of that predicted over the lifetime of the

population. This uncertainty is much greater for those exposed when young. For a working population aged 18–64 years, the total fatal cancer risk predicted over a lifetime is 5.0 10^{-2} Sv^{-1}, whereas that up to 40 years following exposure is 3.0 10^{-2} Sv^{-1}. The number of non-fatal radiation-induced cancers is estimated to be about two-thirds of the number of fatal cancers.

14   The uncertainties in these cancer risk estimates should be stressed. The total cancer risk could be up to a factor of about two less than the lifetime projected value given here. Uncertainty concerning the choice of DDREF could mean that the risks are too high or too low by a factor of about two, whereas for individual cancer types, there is an additional uncertainty factor of two or more associated with the transfer of risks across populations and statistical uncertainties in the source data. However, the latter uncertainties, together with that concerning the projection of risks over time, are considerably less for leukaemia. These uncertainties are likely to be reduced by continued follow-up of populations exposed to high doses, along with combined analysis of data on groups exposed to low doses at low dose rates, such as radiation workers.

15   A large amount of data on the induction of lung cancer following radon exposure is provided by many studies of occupationally exposed miners. Although there is still some uncertainty in risk assessments concerning the interaction of radon and smoking and the possibility of an exposure rate effect, the estimate of fatal lung cancer over a lifetime associated with indoor radon exposure is taken here as 3.5 10^{-4} WLM^{-1}; this arises from applying the risk model of ICRP[5] to a UK population and is also the value recommended by the BEIR IV Committee[6]. Even though many epidemiological studies of indoor radon exposure and lung cancer are currently in progress, it will be some years before all the results are published and then combined in a pooled analysis. As regards cancers other than lung, whereas a correlation study based on small areas throughout Britain has not shown a statistically significant correlation between indoor radon and childhood leukaemia, several large case–control and cohort studies that involve individual radon assessments are currently being performed.

16   The data relevant to the estimation of the risk of heritable effects following radiation exposure have been reviewed with particular emphasis on the difficulties faced in extrapolating existing animal data to man. Uncertainties on the estimation of doubling doses for genetic effects have been reviewed in the light of the recent re-analysis of the genetic data from the offspring of atomic bomb survivors, new data on the nature of radiation-induced germ line mutations and their implications for the relative radiosensitivity of genetic endpoints in animal systems. Recent discussions of the question whether risk coefficients derived from existing animal data might overestimate the genetic effects of radiation in man are outlined but, given the uncertainties, the risk coefficients recommended by ICRP[5] for low dose rate, low LET exposures are applied. Thus, the risk of genetic disease in the reproductive population over all generations (including individuals irradiated *in utero*) is calculated to be 2.4 10^{-2} Gy^{-1}: for the whole population the risk will be 40% of this, ie 1.0 10^{-2} Gy^{-1}, and for a working population about 25% of this, ie 0.6 10^{-2} Gy^{-1}. On the basis of animal data, these risk coefficients should be increased by a factor of three for high dose and high dose rate exposures.

17   Experimental and epidemiological studies on cancer in offspring following parental radiation exposure have also been considered. The uncertainties faced in the

interpretation of these data are such that it would be premature to include them in the estimation of heritable risk.

18   Studies on children exposed *in utero* as a consequence of the Japanese atomic bomb explosions have shown a dose dependent increase in the incidences of severe mental retardation (SMR) and IQ loss. For SMR, this phenomenon is most clearly evident following exposure during the 8–15 week period of gestation; before this period there is no evidence of excess SMR and lower frequencies were recorded during the 16–25 week period. Evaluation of these data leads to the conclusion that a radiation dose threshold probably exists for exposure during the 16–25 week period but that the evidence for a threshold in the 8–15 week period is equivocal; on this basis it is assumed that the *in utero* neurological response increases with dose without a threshold. The data on SMR incidence in the Japanese children are broadly consistent with a dose-related shift in the IQ of around 30 points Gy^{-1} (low LET). Possible cellular mechanisms underlying these responses are discussed.

19   The limited human data on the *in utero* induction of malformation are discussed together with animal studies. It is considered that for low dose and low dose rate exposures the risk of malformation is very small when compared with the natural, spontaneously arising risk.

20   The childhood cancer risk following *in utero* irradiation has been based on excess risk data derived from the Oxford Survey of Childhood Cancers and dose estimates to the fetus as a consequence of obstetric X-ray exposure. The estimated risk of leukaemia is $2.5 \ 10^{-2} \ Gy^{-1}$ (low LET), and of other cancers $3.5 \ 10^{-2} \ Gy^{-1}$; half of these cases are assumed to be fatal. These risk coefficients are directly applicable to low doses and dose rates. To this risk of fatal childhood cancer must be added that occurring later in life (beyond 15 years of age). The data on the atomic bomb survivors suggest that the overall risk of fatal cancer following exposure *in utero* may exceed that in the first 15 years of life by a factor up to four; there are, however, considerable uncertainties in projecting lifetime risks from current data and this factor may perhaps be nearer two. The risk estimates up to 15 years are therefore considered more reliable.

21   It is assumed that hereditary risks following *in utero* exposure are the same as that after birth, ie $2.4 \ 10^{-2} \ Sv^{-1}$.

REFERENCES

1   UNSCEAR. Sources, effects and risks of ionizing radiation. 1988 Report to the General Assembly, with annexes. New York, United Nations (1988).

2   BEIR V. Health effects of exposure to low levels of ionising radiation. Washington DC, NAS/NRC (1990).

3   ICRP. 1990 Recommendations of the International Commission on Radiological Protection. ICRP Publication 60, *Ann. ICRP,* **21**, Nos 1–3 (1991).

4   Stather, J W, Muirhead, C R, Edwards, A A, Harrison, J D, Lloyd, D C, and Wood, N R. Health effects models developed from the 1988 UNSCEAR report. Chilton, NRPB-R226 (1988) (London, HMSO).

5   ICRP. Lung cancer risk from indoor exposures to radon daughters. ICRP Publication 50. *Ann. ICRP,* **17**, No. 1 (1987).

6   BEIR IV. Health risks of radon and other internally deposited alpha-emitters. Washington DC, NAS/NRC (1988).

Appendix A

ANALYSES OF CANCER MORTALITY AMONG THE JAPANESE ATOMIC BOMB SURVIVORS

1   The Radiation Effects Research Foundation (RERF) in Japan has released a disk containing detailed data on cancer mortality among the Japanese atomic bomb survivors up to 1985, based on the DS86 dose estimates[1]. The data files consist of person-years and numbers of deaths from various cancer types, subdivided by age at exposure, sex, calendar period, city (Hiroshima/Nagasaki) and dose kerma (ie dose-in-air), together with factors to convert dose kerma to organ dose for various organs. These data were used by the BEIR V Committee[2] in deriving models for the risks of leukaemia, breast cancer, respiratory cancer, digestive cancers, and the grouping of all other cancers. Since some of the cancer groupings considered by the BEIR V Committee were quite large, further analyses have been carried out for this report based on the above data. In particular, the following cancer types have been studied: lung, stomach, colon, and the grouping of all cancers other than leukaemia, bone, breast, colon, lung, skin and stomach cancer. The models so chosen form the basis of the risk estimates presented in Tables 4.4 and 4.5 of the main text.

2   General relative risk (RR) models of the following form have been considered:

$$RR = 1 + \alpha\, d \exp\left(\Sigma_i\, \beta_i x_i\right) \tag{A1}$$

where d denotes dose, x_1, x_2, etc, denote covariates such as sex, age at exposure and time since exposure (or functions thereof), and α and β_1, β_2, etc, are coefficients estimated by fitting this model to the data. Under this model the radiation-induced risk is assumed to vary in a linear manner with dose d; this is in line with the results of analyses for solid cancers as a whole by Pierce and Vaeth[3] (see Chapter 4, paragraph 47).

3   If none of the covariates varies with time since exposure, then equation A1 specifies a model under which the relative risk is constant with time since exposure. However, if one or more of the covariates does vary with time since exposure, then equation A1 encompasses a more general class of models such that the relative risk is time dependent – for example, models under which the excess relative risk ultimately diminishes with increasing time since exposure. It is helpful to specify the risk model in terms of relative risk (rather than absolute risk), since no assumptions need to be made about the form of the baseline cancer rates when fitting this model to the data[4,5]. The model fitting was performed using the program AMFIT, which is part of the EPICURE package[6] and which was also used by the BEIR V Committee in its analyses[2]. As in the latter analyses, those Japanese atomic bomb survivors with DS86 organ doses in excess of 4 Sv were excluded from the analyses described below, because of indications of an apparent levelling-off in the dose response beyond 4 Sv that may be due to errors in the estimates of such high doses and/or to cell killing[2]. Furthermore, those survivors aged more than 75 years were excluded, as in the BEIR V report, because of doubts over the validity of cause-of-death information at these ages. To allow for a minimal latent period of 10 years for solid cancers, only data from 1955 onwards were considered.

4   The goodness-of-fit of the models considered is summarised in Tables A1–A4 in terms of the deviance[7] – the smaller the deviance, the better the fit. Improvements in fit can be obtained by including a progressively larger number of covariates in the model specified in equation A1, so making the model more general. However, after a certain stage, the fit is not improved to a statistically significant extent by including further covariates. A test of whether a model with a given set of covariates provides a statistically significant improvement in fit over a model with a subset of these covariates arises from comparing the difference in deviance between these models with the chi-squared distribution, with degrees of freedom equal to the difference in the number of covariates (this also equals the difference in the degrees of freedom associated with the fit of the two models)[7].

5   As well as empirical models derived solely on the basis of the goodness-of-fit to the data, some mechanistic models were also considered in order to provide an illustration of this approach (see Chapter 4, paragraphs 12–15). In particular, Armitage–Doll multistage models were examined, for which the relative risk (RR) was taken to be of the following form:

$$RR = 1 + \alpha\, d\exp\left[(j-1)\ln b + (k-j-1)\ln t - (k-1)\ln a\right] \qquad (A2)$$

where b denotes age at exposure, t denotes time since exposure, and a denotes attained age[8]. Equation A2 is a special case of equation 4.1 under which the excess relative risk varies in a linear manner with dose, d. It is also a special case of equation A1 and so this model can be fitted in the same manner as the empirical models above. Since the data lack sufficient statistical power to distinguish between the fits for different values of k (the number of stages in the multistage model), results are presented here solely for $k = 5$ (ie a five-stage model). Various values for j (the stage at which radiation is assumed to act) have been considered including non-integer values, although risk calculations were performed only for integer values of j. Also, as well as examining whether the dose–response coefficient, α, differs between sexes, study has been made of whether there is evidence that the stage at which radiation acts, j, is sex specific. The fit of other types of multistage models to the Japanese data has been considered by Thomas[9], based on the grouping of all solid cancers rather than on individual cancer types, while Little *et al*[10] have fitted the Armitage–Doll model both to the Japanese data and to data for three other radiation-exposed cohorts.

Covariates	Deviance	Degrees of freedom
a —	638.33	1891
b Sex	636.96	1890
c Sex + log (time since exposure)	635.25	1889
d Sex + linear age at exposure	633.94	1889
e Sex + log (time since exposure) + linear age at exposure	635.10	1888
Armitage–Doll models		
f $k = 5, j = 3$	637.97	1891
g Sex + ($k = 5, j = 3$)	636.66	1890
h Sex + ($k = 5, j = 5$, males 2, females)	634.77	1890

TABLE A1
Goodness-of-fit of models for lung cancer mortality among the Japanese atomic bomb survivors

<table>
<tr><td>TABLE A2
Goodness-of-fit of models for colon cancer mortality among the Japanese atomic bomb survivors</td><td colspan="3">

Covariates	Deviance	Degrees of freedom
a —	296.60	1924
b Sex	296.60	1923
c Sex + linear age at exposure	292.61	1922
d Sex + linear age at exposure + log (time since exposure)	287.30	1921
e Sex + A	293.26	1922
Armitage–Doll models		
f k = 5, j = 2	293.44	1924
g Sex + (k = 5, j = 2)	293.44	1923

</td></tr>
</table>

Note A is a function of age at exposure defined in relation to equation A4.

<table>
<tr><td>TABLE A3
Goodness-of-fit of models for stomach cancer mortality among the Japanese atomic bomb survivors</td><td colspan="3">

Covariates	Deviance	Degrees of freedom
a —	1082.00	1912
b Sex	1080.68	1911
c Sex + linear age at exposure	1075.01	1910
d Sex + linear age at exposure + log (time since exposure)	1074.79	1909
e Sex + A	1070.54	1910
Armitage–Doll models		
f k = 5, j = 2	1075.11	1912
g Sex + (k = 5, j = 2)	1074.17	1911

</td></tr>
</table>

Note A is a function of age at exposure defined in relation to equation A4.

<table>
<tr><td>TABLE A4
Goodness-of-fit of models for mortality from cancers other than leukaemia, bone, breast, colon, lung, skin and stomach cancer among the Japanese atomic bomb survivors</td><td colspan="3">

Covariates	Deviance	Degrees of freedom
a —	1267.07	1891
b Linear age at exposure	1258.96	1890
c Sex + linear age at exposure	1258.35	1889
d Sex + linear age at exposure + log (time since exposure)	1258.10	1888
e E	1260.31	1890
Armitage–Doll models		
f k = 5, j = 2	1259.96	1891
g k = 5, j = 1	1258.39	1891
h Sex + (k = 5, j = 1)	1257.55	1890

</td></tr>
</table>

Note E is a function of age at exposure defined in relation to equation A5.

150

Lung cancer

6   Table A1 summarises the goodness-of-fit of various models of the form given in equation A1 for lung cancer mortality among the atomic bomb survivors. Including covariates corresponding to sex, time since exposure and age at exposure each improves the fit, although in none of the cases is the reduction in deviance significant at the 5% level. Based on these results it was decided to use a model of the form of model c in Table A1 to describe the variation in the relative risk, RR, of lung cancer. In particular, the BEIR V relative risk model for respiratory cancer was chosen, namely:

$$RR = 1 + \alpha\, d \exp [\beta_1 \log (t/20) + \beta_2 s] \tag{A3}$$

where t = years after exposure.

$$s = \begin{cases} 0, \text{males} \\ 1, \text{females} \end{cases}$$

$\alpha = 0.636, \beta_1 = -1.437, \beta_2 = 0.711.$

Under this model the relative risk, RR, is higher for females than for males, and decreases with increasing time since exposure.

7   For Armitage–Doll models of the form given in equation A2 with $k = 5$ stages, the best fit on the assumption of a single-stage effect of radiation that is the same for both sexes arises for $j = 3.12$, suggesting an effect at the third stage. However, examination of the data for males and females separately gives some indication that the stage at which radiation appears to act may differ between sexes; the best fit of j is 5.01 for males and 2.44 for females. Whilst the reduction in deviance (3.58 on 2 degrees of freedom) is not significant at the 5% level, inspection of the deviance as a function of j shows quite different patterns for the two sexes; the male data are indicative of a late stage effect and the female data of an earlier effect at stage 2 or 3. Since the results for females are in line with those for other cancers (see below), it may be that the results for males are an artefact owing to a confounding effect of smoking. However, since smoking data were not available to allow further analysis of the joint effect of radiation and smoking on the male lung cancer risk, the Armitage–Doll model with a fifth-stage effect for males and a second-stage effect for females was used for the illustrative calculations in Table 4.6.

Colon cancer

8   Table A2 shows the goodness-of-fit of various models for colon cancer mortality. Whilst there is little evidence that sex affects the relative risk (comparison of models b and a), the reduction in deviance owing to the inclusion of age at exposure is significant at the 5% level (comparison of models c and b). Model e, which is of the same form as the BEIR V model for digestive cancers, has a deviance similar to that of model c, and it was decided to use the BEIR V model to describe the relative risk, RR, of colon cancer, ie

$$RR = 1 + \alpha\, d \exp [\beta_1 s + \beta_2 A] \tag{A4}$$

where $s = \begin{cases} 0, \text{males} \\ 1, \text{females} \end{cases}$

$$A = \begin{cases} 0, \text{for age at exposure } (b) \leq 25 \text{ y,} \\ b - 25, \text{for } 25 < b \leq 35, \\ 10, \text{for } b > 35, \end{cases}$$

$\alpha = 0.809, \beta_1 = 0.553, \beta_2 = -0.198.$

Under this model the relative risk is higher for females than for males and for those irradiated at younger ages than at older ages.

9   Comparison of models d and c in Table A2 does, however, provide some evidence of a decrease in the relative risk with time since exposure. A similar pattern arises under the best-fitting Armitage–Doll model. Out of 5 stages, the best estimate of the stage at which radiation acts is $j = 1.87$. There is little suggestion of any difference in the value of j between sexes. Consequently the illustrative calculations in Table 4.6 were based on radiation acting at the second out of 5 stages.

Stomach cancer

10   Table A3 shows the goodness-of-fit of various models for stomach cancer mortality. Although the reduction in deviance from including sex as a covariate is not significant at the 5% level (comparison of models b and a), that arising from including age at exposure as a linear covariate is significant at the above level (comparison of models c and b). A lower deviance still arises for model e, which is of the form of the BEIR V model for digestive cancers. Comparison of the deviances for models d and c provides little indication that the relative risk varies with time since exposure. It was therefore decided to use the BEIR V model as given by equation A4 to describe the relative risk of stomach cancer.

11   For Armitage–Doll models with a total of 5 stages, the best estimate of j (the stage at which radiation acts) is 1.87. There is little suggestion that the value of j differs between sexes. Consequently the illustrative calculations in Table 4.6 were based on radiation acting at the second out of 5 stages.

All cancers other than leukaemia, bone, breast, colon, lung, skin and stomach cancer

12   Table A4 shows the goodness-of-fit of various models for this cancer grouping. It should be noted that this grouping includes thyroid cancer since the LSS data file did not specify thyroid cancer separately and so did not allow it to be excluded. Consequently lifetime risks for the above grouping but excluding thyroid cancer were derived by applying the relative risk derived for the grouping including thyroid cancer to baseline rates excluding thyroid cancer.

13   Comparison of the deviances for models b and a in Table A4 shows that there is strong evidence ($p < 0.01$) for an effect of age at exposure on the relative risk, RR. However, the results for models c and d provide little evidence that RR varies with sex or time since exposure within the follow-up period. Model e, which is of the same form as the BEIR V model for the grouping of all cancers other than leukaemia, breast, respiratory and digestive cancers, has a deviance similar to that of model b. Consequently the BEIR V model was used to describe the relative risk for the group of cancers considered in this section, ie

$$RR = 1 + \alpha \, d \exp(\beta_1 E) \tag{A5}$$

where $E = \begin{cases} 0, \text{for age at exposure } (b) \leq 10 \text{ y,} \\ b - 10, \text{for } b > 10, \end{cases}$

$\alpha = 1.220, \beta_1 = -0.0464.$

Under this model the relative risk decreases with increasing age at exposure (after age 10 years).

14   For the Armitage–Doll models, the best estimate of the stage j at which radiation acts (out of a total of 5 stages) is 1.37. There is little indication that the value of j varies between sexes. Although it is difficult to distinguish between the goodness-of-fit of models with $j = 1$ and $j = 2$ (ie g and h in Table A4), the former was chosen for the illustrative calculations in Table 4.6 because of the lower deviance. The main difference between the form of these models is that, in comparison with the latter model, the former model predicts a slower increase in the relative risk soon after exposure and then a shallower decrease in the relative risk at long times after exposure (see Thomas[8]).

ACKNOWLEDGEMENT

15   This report makes use of data obtained from the Radiation Effects Research Foundation (RERF) in Hiroshima, Japan. RERF is a private foundation funded equally by the Japanese Ministry of Health and Welfare and the American Department of Energy through the National Academy of Sciences. The conclusions in this report are those of the authors and do not necessarily reflect the scientific judgement of RERF or its funding agencies.

REFERENCES

1   Shimizu, Y, Kato, H, and Schull, W J. Life Span Study Report 11, Part II: Cancer mortality in the years 1950–1985 based on the recently revised doses (DS86). Hiroshima, Radiation Effects Research Foundation, Report TR5-88 (1988).

2   BEIR V. Health effects of exposure to low levels of ionising radiation. Washington DC, NAS/NRC (1990).

3   Pierce, D A, and Vaeth, M. The shape of the cancer mortality dose–response curve for the A-bomb survivors. *Radiat. Res.*, **126**, 36–42 (1991).

4   Cox, D R. Regression models and life-tables (with discussion). *J. Roy. Stat. Soc.*, **B34**, 187–220 (1972).

5   Muirhead, C R, and Darby, S C. Modelling the relative and absolute risks of radiation-induced cancers. *J. Roy. Stat. Soc.*, **A150**, 83–118 (1987).

6   Preston, D L, Lubin, J H, and Pierce, D A. *EPICURE User's Guide*. Seattle, Hirosoft Corporation (1991).

7   McCullagh, P, and Nelder, J A. *Generalised Linear Models* (2nd edition). London, Chapman and Hall (1989).

8   Thomas, D C. Temporal effects and interactions in cancer: Implications of carcinogenic models. IN *Environmental Epidemiology: Risk Assessment* (Eds R L Prentice and A S Whittemore), Philadelphia, SIAM, pp 107–21 (1982).

9   Thomas, D C. A model for dose rate and duration of exposure effects in radiation carcinogenesis. *Environ. Health Perspect.*, **87**, 163–71 (1990).

10   Little, M P, Hawkins, M M, Charles, M W, and Hildreth, N G. Fitting the Armitage–Doll model to radiation-exposed cohorts and implications for population cancer risks. *Radiat. Res.*, **132**, 207–21 (1992).

Appendix B

EPIDEMIOLOGICAL STUDIES OF LOW DOSE RATE EXPOSURE AND CANCER

1   As pointed out in Chapter 4, most studies in radiation epidemiology are of populations exposed at high dose rate. Studies of low dose rate exposure, however, generally involve low doses; because of the likely low excess risks, such studies are likely to be hampered by lack of statistical power and possibly also by confounding factors. It is therefore still necessary in deriving cancer risk estimates to use high dose rate studies, with a correction factor derived from radiobiology used for the extrapolation to low dose rates. However, examination of the results of the low dose rate studies can provide a check on the risks derived by extrapolation from high dose rate studies. A brief review of some low dose rate studies follows.

Occupational exposures

2   Studies of radiologists in the UK[1] and the USA[2] and of medical X-ray workers in China[3] have shown raised risks for leukaemia and the grouping of all cancers. Although the dose information is not particularly good, it is thought that some of the early radiologists and the Chinese workers received doses in excess of 1 Gy, but possibly at high dose rates. Several studies have been conducted of nuclear industry workers. In the USA, Gilbert *et al*[4] performed a joint analysis of data for about 36 000 workers at the Hanford site, Oak Ridge National Laboratory and Rocky Flats weapons plant. Neither for the grouping of all cancers nor for leukaemia was there an indication of an increasing trend in risk with dose. However, the upper limit of the 90% confidence interval for the excess relative risk per unit dose was similar to the corresponding value for the Japanese atomic bomb survivors in the case of all cancers and slightly less than the value from Japan in the case of leukaemia. In terms of lifetime risk for a worker population, the upper limit of the 90% confidence interval from the American study corresponded to a value of about $8.2 \ 10^{-2} \ Sv^{-1}$ for all cancers and $0.6 \ 10^{-2} \ Sv^{-1}$ for leukaemia. Consequently the study of American nuclear industry workers did not indicate that risks calculated on the basis of a linear dose–response model from the Japanese data are seriously in error, and, particularly in the case of leukaemia, suggested the need for a dose and dose rate effectiveness factor (DDREF) greater than unity at low doses and low dose rates.

3   A recent study of just over 95 000 individuals on the UK National Registry for Radiation Workers (NRRW) examined cancer mortality in relation to dose[5]. For all malignant neoplasms, the trend in the relative risk with dose was positive but was not statistically significant ($p = 0.10$). Based on a relative risk projection model, the central estimate of the lifetime risk from these data was 10% Sv^{-1}, which is 2.5 times the value of 4% Sv^{-1} cited by ICRP[6] for risks associated with exposure of workers (based on the application of a DDREF of 2 to the Japanese data). The 90% confidence interval for the NRRW-derived risk ranged from a negative value to about six times the ICRP value. For leukaemia (excluding chronic lymphatic leukaemia (CLL) which does not appear to be radiation-inducible), the trend in risk with dose was statistically significant ($p = 0.03$). Based on a BEIR V type projection model[7], the central estimate of the corresponding

lifetime leukaemia risk was 0.76% Sv^{-1} which is 1.9 times the ICRP value for a worker population (0.4% Sv^{-1}), with 90% confidence limits ranging from just above zero to about six times the ICRP value. There was also an indication of an increasing trend with dose in the risk of multiple myeloma ($p = 0.06$); the estimated trend in the relative risk was about three times that obtained from the Japanese survivor data under a linear dose–response model, with 90% confidence limits ranging from just under zero to twenty times the Japanese value. An increasing trend in multiple myeloma risk with dose was similarly found in the American study[4] ($p < 0.05$).

4   The National Registry for Radiation Workers therefore provides evidence of raised risks of leukaemia and multiple myeloma associated with occupational exposure to radiation, but, as with the combined study of American workers[4], is consistent with the risk estimates for low dose/dose rate exposures derived by ICRP[6] from the Japanese survivor data. In particular, combining the NRRW and American results produces central estimates for the lifetime risk of 4.9 10^{-2} Sv^{-1} (90% CI < 0, 18) for all cancers and 0.30 10^{-2} Sv^{-1} (90% CI < 0, 1.04) for leukaemia excluding CLL[8], which are similar to the ICRP risk estimates.

Background radiation

5   Studies of exposure to natural radiation (other than radon) have generally involved a search for any geographical correlation with cancer rates. Such studies can be difficult to interpret owing to the effect of confounding factors such as socio-demographic variables and other factors that vary geographically; for example, altitude appeared to act as a confounder in a study of background radiation in the USA[9]. Another potential problem, namely population migration, was addressed by a study in China of stable populations in two areas with different levels of background radiation[10]; no excess of leukaemia was found in the area with the higher background level. In a similar study, Wang *et al*[11] found that the prevalence of thyroid nodules, which have been linked in other studies with the development of thyroid cancer, was similar among about 1000 women aged 50–65 years who had resided their entire lives in a high background area and a similar number of women who had lived in a normal background area. The cumulative doses to the thyroid in the two areas were about 140 and 50 mGy, respectively. However, there was an indication of higher levels of chromosome aberrations in the high background area. The effects of population migration might also be thought to be less in a study of childhood cancer than for cancers at older ages; furthermore, since the variation in childhood cancer rates is less than that for adult cancers, the effect of confounding may also be reduced. Although Knox *et al*[12] claimed to show a statistically significant correlation between childhood cancer and gamma dose rate in Great Britain, the statistical methodology used was non-standard. An analysis of childhood leukaemia and natural radiation in Great Britain[13], based on data at the district level and using standard methods, did not show any statistically significant correlations with indoor or outdoor gamma dose rate (see also Chapter 4, paragraph 96). However, it should be noted that studies of the effects of exposure to background radiation are likely to lack statistical power to detect small excess risks.

Environmental exposures

6   Most studies of environmental exposures have also involved a search for geographical correlations (as in the background radiation studies) and/or temporal

trends in cancer rates. For example, Darby *et al*[14] examined temporal trends in childhood leukaemia in the Nordic countries in relation to fallout from atmospheric nuclear weapons testing during the 1950s and the 1960s. They concluded that there was some evidence of a raised risk associated with the 'high' exposure period, when children would have received a dose from fallout of about 1.5 mSv, compared with the proximate 'medium' exposure period, when the dose received would have been about 0.5 mSv (relative risk for ages 0–14 years:1.07, 95% CI 1.00–1.14). These data are consistent with a relative risk of 1.03 predicted under the BEIR V leukaemia model[7]; although the central estimate from this study is larger than the BEIR V value, the difference can be explained by the different follow-up times upon which these two values are based (0–7 years and 5–15 years, respectively).

7   In contrast to descriptive studies based on geographical or temporal comparisons of environmental exposures and cancer rates, Stevens *et al*[15] performed a case–control study of leukaemia in Utah in relation to fallout from nuclear weapons tests at the Nevada test site. A weak association was found between the estimated bone marrow dose and leukaemia mortality at all ages, of all types and over all time periods. Among other analyses, the greatest excess risk was found for acute leukaemia deaths before 1964 at ages less than 20 years with estimated doses in the range 6–30 mGy (odds ratio 7.82, 95% CI 1.90–32.2). The central estimate of risk is about twice that predicted under the BEIR V model for leukaemia[7], derived from the Japanese atomic bomb survivor data with a low dose extrapolation factor of two, but the confidence interval includes the BEIR V value.

Conclusions

8   Although some studies of populations exposed to low LET radiation at low dose rates provide indications of excess cancer risks, notably for leukaemia, the statistical uncertainties are sufficiently large for the risk estimates to be consistent with those derived by extrapolation from high dose rate studies based on a DDREF of two, as well as with values differing by at least a factor of two, and although the low dose rate studies are not strong enough to allow the derivation of risk estimates in view of these uncertainties, such studies are generally consistent with the estimates derived by ICRP.

REFERENCES

1   Smith, P G, and Doll, R. Mortality from cancer and all causes among British radiologists. *Br. J. Radiol.*, **54**, 187–94 (1981).

2   Matanoski, G M, Sartwell, P, Elliott, E, Tomascia, J, and Sternberg, A. Cancer risks in radiologists and radiation workers. IN *Radiation Carcinogenesis: Epidemiology and Biological Significance* (Eds J D Boice and J F Fraumeni). New York, Raven Press, pp 83–96 (1984).

3   Wang, J-X, Inskip, P D, Boice, J D, Li, B-X, Zhang, J-Y, and Fraumeni, J F. Cancer incidence among medical diagnostic x-ray workers in China, 1950 to 1985. *Int. J. Cancer*, **45**, 889–95 (1990).

4   Gilbert, E S, Fry, S A, Wiggs, L D, Voelz, G L, Cragle, D L, and Petersen, G R. Analyses of combined mortality data on workers at the Hanford site, Oak Ridge National Laboratory and Rocky Flats nuclear weapons plant. *Radiat. Res.*, **120**, 19–35 (1989).

5   Kendall, G M, Muirhead, C R, MacGibbon, B H, O'Hagan, J A, Conquest, A J, Goodill, A A, Butland, B K, Fell, T P, Jackson, D A, Webb, M A, Haylock, R G E, Thomas, J M, and Silk, T J. Mortality and occupational exposure to radiation: first analysis of the National Registry for Radiation Workers. *Br. Med. J.*, **304**, 220–25 (1992).

6   ICRP. 1990 Recommendations of the International Commission on Radiological Protection. ICRP Publication 60. *Ann. ICRP*, **21**, Nos 1–3 (1991).

7   BEIR V. Health effects of exposure to low levels of ionising radiation. Washington DC, NAS/NRC (1990).

8   Kendall, G M, Muirhead, C R, MacGibbon, B H, O'Hagan, J A, Conquest, A J, Goodill, A A, Butland, B K, Fell, T P, Jackson, D A, Webb, M A, Haylock, R G E, Thomas, J M, and Silk, T J. First analysis of the National Registry for Radiation Workers: Occupational exposure to ionising radiation and mortality. Chilton, NRPB-R251 (1992) (London, HMSO).

9   Weinberg, C R, Brown, K G, and Hoel, D G. Altitude, radiation and mortality from cancer and heart disease. *Radiat. Res.*, **112**, 381–90 (1987).

10   Wei, L, Yongru, Z, Zufan, T, *et al.* Epidemiological investigation of radiological effects in high background areas of Yangjiang, China. *J. Radiat. Res.*, **31**, 119 (1990).

11   Wang, Z, Boice, J D, Wei, L, *et al.* Thyroid nodularity and chromosome aberrations among women in areas of high background radiation in China. *J. Natl Cancer Inst.*, **82**, 478 (1990).

12   Knox, E G, Stewart, A M, Gilman, E A, and Kneale, G W. Background radiation and childhood cancer. *J. Radiol. Prot.*, **8**, 9–18 (1988).

13   Muirhead, C R, Butland, B K, Green, B M R, and Draper, G J. Childhood leukaemia and natural radiation. *Lancet*, **337**, 503–4 (1991).

14   Darby, S C, Olsen, J H, Doll R, Thakrar, B, de Nully Brown, P, Storm, H H, Barlow, L, Langmark, F, Teppo, L, and Tulinius, H. Trends in childhood leukaemia in the Nordic countries in relation to fallout from atmospheric nuclear weapons testing. *Br. Med. J.*, **304**, 1005 (1992).

15   Stevens, W, Thomas, D C, Lyon, J L, Till, J E, Kerber, R A, Simon, S L, Lloyd, R D, Elghany, N A, and Preston-Martin, S. Leukemia in Utah and radioactive fallout from the Nevada test site. *JAMA*, **264**, 585–91 (1990).